Xiao-fan Zong

CHINESE MEDICAL

Your Health in Your Hand

PALMISTRY

法定

八卦宜滿明堂宜深掌紋宜秀掌色宜鮮賓主宜配指節宜不露指肉宜明嫩掌宜有肉掌背宜厚不露筋骨掌紋深秀

成字成卯成令俱宜紋溢掌背主破耗紋沖四指主有功名紋亂坤位主好色紋亂巽位主破財書載掌紋俱皆穿鑿。

開門紅潤出入求富貴用兵吉生門休門亦然

景門青暗出入必防災盜

死門青暗主死亡

傷門青暗必有刑剋諸事不利

驚門青暗主大驚恐

杜門青暗不利出行大破財

Published by:

Blue Poppy Press
1775 Linden Ave. Boulder, CO 80304
(303) 447-8372

First Edition June, 1995

ISBN 0-936185-64-3
Library of Congress #-95-774C8

Copyright © Blue Poppy Press

The information in this book is given in good faith. However, the translators and the publishers cannot abe held responsible for any error or omission. Nor can they be held in any way responsible for treatment given on the basis of information contained in this book. The publishers make this information available to English readers for scholarly and research purposes only.

The publishers do not advocate nor endorse self-medication by laypersons. Chinese medicine is a professional medicine. Laypersons interested in availing themselves of the treatments described in this book should seek out a qualified professional practitioner of Chinese medicine.

COMP Designation: Connotative translation

Printed at Johnson Printing, Boulder, CO

10, 9, 8, 7, 6, 5, 4, 3, 2

Dedication

This work is dedicated to my parents,
Chen Yu-fen & Zong Tian-xiang,
for their relentless efforts in emphasizing my education.

Z.X.F.

Preface

This book is the first in English to deal specifically with the diagnosis of disease through Chinese palmistry and Chinese fingernail diagnosis. It is meant for all those interested in palmistry in general and in Chinese medical palmistry in particular. It is especially meant for practitioners of Traditional Chinese Medicine or TCM.

Several years ago, a colleague and I were discussing the seemingly miraculous diagnoses of a famous old Chinese doctor practicing in the United States. I was saying how wonderful this old gentleman's pulse diagnosis was, given what he frequently told patients after having felt their pulses for several minutes. But my friend, who had studied in this *lao yi sheng*'s clinic, said that this doctor was also a master of Chinese palmistry and physiognomy. While taking the pulse with the patient's palm up, some of what he knew about each patient was read in the shape of their hands and the lines on their palms. Having studied Western palmistry many years ago and still occasionally entertaining friends and acquaintances with it, this piqued my interest in Chinese medical palmistry and from that time forward I kept my eyes peeled for any books on the subject.

A couple of years ago, one of my teachers in Shanghai, knowing my interest in the medical application of Chinese palmistry, sent me several books that had recently been published in the People's Republic of China. However, due to a number of seemingly more important projects, these languished on my shelves until Zong Xiao-fan and her husband, Gary Liscum, mentioned they were interested in doing some translation for Blue Poppy Press and asked if there was any project I had in mind. Zong Xiao-fan was trained as a translator at the Second Foreign Language Institute in Beijing and Gary Liscum is a practitioner of acupuncture and Chinese medicine who has studied in China and has more than a dozen years of clinical experience.

Thus I gave Xiao-fan and Gary my various Chinese books on medical palmistry. I asked them to extract the best and most usable information from each and then to compile an entirely new book out of that information written with Western readers and especially Western practitioners of TCM in mind. I felt sure that the combination of Xiao-fan's expertise as a translator and

Gary's clinical experience both in China and the United States was a formula for the creation of an excellent new book on this topic.

This book is the fruit of that collaboration. It is with pleasure that I introduce to Western readers Zong Xiao-fan and Gary Liscum. May this book only be the first created through their combined abilities and efforts, and may it help practitioners of all systems clarify their patients' diagnoses and constitutional predispositions.

Bob Flaws
Jan. 6, 1995

Contents

Book One
Chinese Medical Palmistry

Book Two
Chinese Fingernail Diagnosis

Contents

Introduction

This book is an introductory guide to the practical application of Chinese medical palmistry. Visual examination by the unaided eye is one of the four basic methods of diagnosis in Traditional Chinese Medicine or TCM. The *Su Wen (Simple Questions)*, one of the oldest and most authoritative classics of Chinese medicine, says that, "If something happens on the interior of the body, it must be reflected on the exterior of the body." Although visual examination within Chinese medicine usually focuses on examining the face, inspecting any areas of the body that are diseased, and especially examining the tongue, in China in recent years there has been renewed interest in examining the hands, palms, and fingernails.

One of the characteristics of Traditional Chinese Medicine is a belief that the part contains the whole. Although Chinese medicine is very old, in the West, this idea is considered very modern and is called holism, as in holisitic health. This is also where we get the word hologram. In holography, one can shine a laser through a part of a holographic image and reproduce the entire image.

Similarly, Chinese doctors for millenia have believed that there are maps of the entire body on various parts of the body. These maps can be used to diagnose the corresponding body parts and, in some cases, such as with hand and ear acupuncture, to even treat those corresponding parts. Technically, these maps are called homunculi or little men. For instance, Chinese doctors believe there are homunculi on the ears, face, eyes, nose, hands, and feet. Some modern Chinese doctors have even found homunculi on the metacarpal bone attached to the index finger and on the femur of the upper leg that can be used to both diagnose and treat the entire body. This belief that there are maps of the entire body on various parts of the body can be called a type of bio-holography. Thus, the idea that one might be able to diagnose patients in part by palmistry is not such a far-fetched one in TCM. In fact, *shou zhen* or hand diagnosis is one of the age-old accepted subdivisions of visual diagnosis within TCM and is included in such modern TCM diagnostic manuals as *Zhong Guo Yi Xue Zhen Fa Da Quan (A Great Collection of Chinese Medical Diagnostic Methods),* published in 1991.

1

A Brief History of Chinese Medical Palmistry

Traditional Chinese palmistry is deeply rooted in yin yang theory, five phase theory, and the eight trigrams of the *Yi Jing (Classic of Change)*. These are different but related systems of universal correspondence whereby all natural phenomena can be arranged in groups, each member of a goup sharing certain inherent qualities or characteristics. Joseph Needham, the greatest sinologist of this century, refers to this as correlative thinking. Because Traditional Chinese Medicine is also rooted in these same theories, it was natural that the ancient Chinese saw correspondences between marks and lines in the palm and medical conditions. As Guo Lin-zong, one of the earliest Chinese writers on palmistry who lived in the late Han Dynasty (206 BCE-220 CE), says, "Humans are parallel to the universe—the universe is man and man is the universe." Thus palmistry has been related to medicine in China from ancient times.

It is said that lines in the palm of the Emperor Shun (2317-2208 BCE) formed the character "to praise." However, as far as the written record is concerned, palmistry in China traces its earliest origins to the Zhou Dynasty (1122-770 BCE) when it was both popular and widespread. The earliest important Chinese discussion of palmistry is found in the *Gu Ge Pian (Writings on the Skeleton)*, also known as *Gu Xiang (Appearances on Bones)*, written by the scholar Wang Chong in the late part of the Han Dynasty (206 BCE-220 CE). According to Wang:

> It is a common belief that fate is difficult to foresee. Far from it, it can easily be known.
> But by what means? By the means of the body and its bones. An inquiry into these
> manifestations leads to a knowledge of fate, just as from a look at a measure, one can
> learn its capacity. By manifestations, I understand the boney configurations.

At this same time, the *Huang Di Nei Jing (Yellow Emperor's Inner Classic)*, the cornerstone of the Chinese medical application of the theory of systematic correspondence to health and medicine, was well established and Zhang Zhong-jing was writing his *Shang Han Lun/Jin Gui Yao Lue (Treatise on Damage by Cold/Essential Formulas from the Golden Chamber)*, the first systematic Chinese discussion of polypharmacy herbal medicine. In fact, the *Nei Jing* contains plentiful references to various medical indications seen in the hands.

Most premodern books on palmistry were not just about palmistry. Rather, sections on

2

palmistry tended to be found as chapters in books on bodily prognostication in general. These books contained sections on face reading or physiognomy (*ren xiang*) as well as sections on reading one's feet, neck, chest, abdomen, navel, lower and upper backs, weight, stance, and body type. The various signs used as indications in these books were referred to as *xiang*. The word *xiang* in Chinese means appearance. When pronounced in a different tone, the word *xiang* means mutual, two things resonating together because they share the same *li* or principles, which then guide and shape their *qi*. Premodern books typically refer to palmistry as *shou xiang*, hand appearances.

Some early Chinese works on physiogonomy and palmistry are the *Yue Bo Dong Zhong Ji (The Moon Wave Cave Record)* by Zhang Zhong-yuan, written during the Three Kingdoms Period (220-265 CE); the *Xiang Jing Shi Si Juan (Fourteen Volumes on Ways of Appearance)* by Lai He, written in the Sui Dynasty (581-618 CE); the *Xiang Fa Ru Men (Entering the Gate of the Method of Appearances)* by Lu Tong-pin of the Tang Dynasty (618-907 CE); the *Shen Xiang Chuan Pian (Complete Writings on Divine Appearances)* by Chen Xi, a.k.a. Chen Tuan, in the Song Dynasty (960-1280 CE); the *Tai Qing Shen Jian (The Divine Mirror of the Tai Qing)* by Wang Bo, also during the Song; and the *Ma Yi Xiang Fa (Ma Yi's Appearances Method)*, which is also attributed to Chen Bo.

In the Chinese medical literature, information on hand diagnosis (*shou zhen*) appears in the famous Sui Dynasty work by Chao Yuan-fang, the *Zhu Bing Yuan Hou Zong Lun (General Treatise on the Origin & Symptoms of Various Diseases)*. In the Tang Dynasty, Wang Chao's *Shui Jing Tu Jue (Water Mirror Diagrams & Rhymes)* describes the method of diagnosing children by observing the veins on the palmar surface of the index finger. This method is now known as *hu kou luo mai zhen fa*, examining the veins at the tiger's mouth method. In the Song Dynasty, the *He Luo Li Shu (Yellow River Principles & Numerology)* related the former and latter heaven eight trigrams of the *Yi Jing (Classic of Change)* to locations on the palm of the hand.

According to Terence Dukes in his *Chinese Hand Analysis*, Chinese palmistry was heavily influenced by Ayurvedic palmistry and hand diagnosis brought to China by Buddhist missionary monks. This influence was greatest in the Sui, Tang, Song, and Yuan Dynasties. For instance, in Duke's list of notable names in Chinese physiognomy, palmistry, and related arts, he lists the Indian Buddhist monks Da Mo (Bodhidharma), Ati Gupta, and Punya Dasa, active in China around 5-600 CE. The system of palmistry these Indian monks brought to China was very similar to that exported from the Middle East to Europe. In China, this system was preserved and propagated by the monks of the Chen Yan sect of Tantric Buddhism. Further, this system was organized on the Buddhist use of the five phases. Thus it is known as the *wu xing pai* or Five Phase School of Chinese palmistry. Today one can still find famous monk practitioners of this art in monsteries in the People's Republic of China. In addition, this art was exported to Taiwan, the Ryukyu Islands, and Japan where it was passed down within the Tantric sect that came to be know as Shingon.

Adherents of this five phase system of palmistry believed and still do that appearances in the hand can reveal the *san hou* or three periods. In other words, one can examine a person's past (*xian zhen*), their present (*zai zhen*), and their future (*lai zhen*). One can also read the hands for information about the four imports or *si tong*. This means that the appearances of the hands can reveal the mind (*xin*) or personality, the body (*shen*), the emotions and thoughts (*yi*), and the qi which unifies all three. Thus it is clear that practitioners of this five phase system of Chinese palmistry did diagnose the physical predispositions and ailments of their subjects.

Numerous other important Chinese books on palmistry were written in succeeding dynasties. For instance, Chen Dan-ye published his well-known book on palmistry, the *Xiang Li Heng Zhen (Mutual Appearances & Their Principles for Measuring the Truth)*, in the Qing Dynasty (1644-1911 CE), and Gao Wei-qing compiled the *Shen Xiang Hui Pian (Collected Writings on Divine Mutual Appearances)* in 1843. In terms of the medical literature, Lin Zhi-han's *Si Zhen Jue Wei (Secrets of Success in the Four Examinations in Minute Detail)* published in 1723 and Zhou Xue-hai's *Xing Se Wai Zhen Jian Mo (Easy Study Form & Color External Examination)* published in 1894 both contained abundant information on hand diagnosis.

Beginning in the seventeenth century, palmistry began to draw the attention of Chinese practitioners of various emerging modern sciences. Anatomists were the first to become interested in palmistry but since have been followed by anthropologists, biologists, and geneticists. These scientists have observed, analyzed, and studied the lines on the palm and have made a number of important contributions to this body of knoweldge. Within the last 20-

30 years in particular, the medical field has begun to show widespread interest in this system of correspondences.

By exploring palmistry from the viewpoint of modern medicine and genetics, further understanding has been gained about the relationship between the lines on the hand and disease. In addition, the use of scientific technology has spurred new developments in the study of palmistry. In China today, biologists, psychologists, and sociologists as well as the above-mentioned anthropologists, geneticists, and physicians are all engaged in substantiating the age-old wisdom on human health and disease contained in Chinese palmistry.

This book is a combination of age-old Chinese lore and modern scientific findings. Some of the indications given in this book are based on yin yang theory, the five phases, or the eight trigrams. Other indications are based on modern clinical observation. This makes modern Chinese medical palmistry a unique blend of ancient and modern knowledge.

Who Can and How to Use Chinese Medical Palmistry

The indications represented in this book can be used by lay people to help determine their individual organic strengths and weaknesses or, in other words, their constitutional predisposition. Knowing how one may tend to become ill, readers of this book can then alter their diet and lifestyle or seek preventive treatment so as to prevent tendencies from becoming realities. Ever since the Warring States Period and the writing of the *Huang Di Nei Jing (The Yellow Emperor's Inner Classic),* prevention has been the highest form of medicine within TCM, and Chinese medical palmistry is well suited to become one of the diagnostic cornerstones of the preventive medicine of the future.

Professional health care practitioners, whether MDs, DCs, NDs, or acupuncturists and TCM practitioners will also find these indications a useful adjunctive diagnositic tool. The hand is readily available and can be examined painlessly, relatively quickly, and without expensive diagnostic machinery. In particular, acupuncturists and TCM practitioners can easily incorporate Chinese medical palm diagnosis into their Chinese pulse diagnosis. While listening to the pulse, the palm is lying face up in front of one. Thus, the practitioner can take a look at the palm while their fingers are on their patient's pulse either before or after they have concentrated their mind on the pulse itself. They do not even have to say that they are doing Chinese medical palm diagnosis if they choose not to.

Like any diagnostic art based on human observation, Chinese medical palmistry takes some practice to master. One should not expect to simply read this book and know all about their own and others' health. After reading this book through from cover to cover, one should start looking at as many hands as possible with this book at their side. Over a period of a few weeks, one should have become skilled at quickly assessing their patients' shape of hand, shape of fingers, major lines in the palm, fingerprints, and nails.

However, Chinese medical palmistry, similar to Chinese pulse reading or Chinese physiognomy, requires both judgment and intuition. One must first analyze the various elements of the hand, such as its lines and shapes, individually. But then one must add these various elements together before concluding, and certainly before stating, that any one sign means this or that. In addition, one's reading of the palm should be tempered by the patient's medical history and information gathered from other diagnostic sources.

In other words, the reader is cautioned not to rely on the information contained in this book alone when making decisions about their own or others' health. Chinese medical palmistry is not a substitute for any other necessay and appropriate professional medical examination or diagnosis. However, as a part of an overall health assessment, Chinese medical palmistry may turn up some very interesting and useful information. This is especially so in the realm of prevention where assessing one's constitutional predispositions is so important.

Many of the indications given in this book are based on modern Western disease categories. However, especially in the section on Chinese fingernail diagnosis, this book also discusses indications in terms of TCM theory. Readers of this book who are unfamiliar with TCM theory are recommended to read Ted Kaptchuk's *Web That Has No Weaver: Understanding Chinese Medicine*. This is the best basic introduction to Traditional Chinese Medicine available in English. In it, the author makes intelligble such Chinese concepts as liver qi stagnation and spleen yang vacuity to Western lay readers.

About This Book

This book is divided into two parts. Book One is about Chinese medical palmistry in general. It presents a basic overview of the medical indications associated with the shape of the hands and fingers, the color of the hands, the various major mounds and lines, and the fingernails. The intent of these indications is primarily to give ideas about an individual's constitutional predispositions. The material in this first section comes from Lin Lang-hui's *Shou Wen Yu Jian Kang (Palmistry & Health)*, Liu Hong-sheng & Liu Hong-xi's *Bai Bing Zi Ce Mi Jue (Secret Tricks for Diagnosing Hundreds of Diseases by Yourself)*, Ma Zhong-xue's *Zhong Guo Yi Xue Zhen Fa Da Quan (A Great Collection of Chinese Medical Diagnostic Techniques)*, and Terence Duke's *Chinese Hand Analysis*.

Book Two is specifically about modern Chinese fingernail diagnosis. Whereas Chinese medical palmistry seeks to identify tendencies and predispositions, Chinese fingernail diagnosis is meant to aid in the diagnosis of actually occuring disease. Rather than saying that a particular disease might occur in the patient's lifetime, fingernail diagnosis seeks to identify what diseases are happening right now. The matierial in this section is based on Wang Wen-hua & Li Jie-jia's *Zhi Jia Zhen Bing (The Fingernail Diagnosis of Disease)*. The TCM translational terminology used in this section of this book and throughout is based on Nigel Wiseman's *Glossary of Chinese Medical Terms and Acupuncture Points*.

Book One

Chinese Medical Palmistry

1
Basic Anatomy of the Hand

Although Chinese palmistry deals with the observable features of the surface anatomy of the hand and wrist, a basic knowledge of the anatomy of the hand's underlying structures is helpful in understanding how these superficial features are created. The underlying skeletal and muscular system give the hand its overall shape and appearance, while the soft tissue, to the degree that it directly attaches to the skin itself, has a great deal to do with the creation of the flexure lines that the color of the hand and, depending on their depth, size, and color, also provide information about specific pathologies.

The Terms *Proximal* & *Distal* in Relationship to the Hands

Western anatomy is a great invention. It has revolutionized the study of medicine, even in Asia. Essentially, Western anatomy is a language for precisely and unambiguously describing the location of any part or piece of the body. In the chapters that follow, there are especially two anatomical terms that appear over and over again and are extremely important for locating positions on the hands. These two terms are *proximal* and *distal*. Proximal and distal are used in Western anatomy primarily for describing the relative locations of parts of the extremities. Proximal means closer to the body trunk and distal means farther away from the body trunk. Thus the hand is distal to the forearm but the palm is proximal to the fingers. And the cuticle of the nail is proximal to the distal terminal edge of the fingernail.

Basic Anatomy of the Hand

1. Bones

The wrist is composed of eight carpal bones. These bones are arranged in two rows transversely. The most proximal row is composed of the scaphoid, lunate, triquetrum, and pisiform. The distal row is composed of the trapezius, trapezoid, capitate, and hamate.

11

The five metacarpal bones form the skeleton of the hand. These metacarpals are numbered one to five starting with the thumb and continuing to the small finger. Fourteen phalanges form the skeleton of the fingers and are numbered similar and corresponding to the metacarpals. Each finger contains three phalanges— proximal, middle, and terminal. However, the thumb contains only two— proximal and terminal.

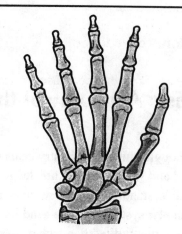

2. Muscles

The muscles of the hand are divided into three groups. The first group are those of the thumb, which form the thenar eminence. The second group are those of the small finger, which form the hypothenar eminence. The third group are the central palmar and interosseous muscles.

A. The thenar muscles are the abductor pollicis brevis, opponens pollicis flexor, pollicis brevis, and adductor pollicis. These muscles flex, abduct, adduct, and oppose the thumb.

B. The hypothenar muscles are the palmar brevis, abductor digiti minimi, flexor digiti minimi brevis, and the opponens digiti minimi. With the exception of the palmaris brevis, these muscles flex, abduct, and oppose the small finger.

C. The central palmar muscles are the lumbricales dorsal and palmar interossei muscles. These muscles act to flex, abduct, and adduct the digits.

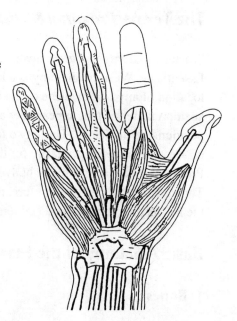

3. Connective tissue

The hand is further composed of retinacula (strong fibrinous bands), synovial sheaths (sheaths that envelop tendons), ligaments, fascial spaces, and aponeuroses (flat fibrinous sheets of connective tissue).

4. Arteries & veins

The superficial venous system that drains the hand is primarily composed of the cephalic, basilic, and meridian antebrachial veins. The palmar venous plexus and the palmar digital veins drain the palmar side of the hand. The palmar digital veins are connected to the dorsum of the hand by the oblique intercapitular veins. The dorsal side of the palm is drained by the dorsal venous network. The veins leading to it are the dorsal digital and dorsal metacarpal veins.   ➡

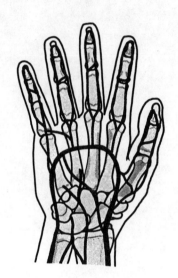

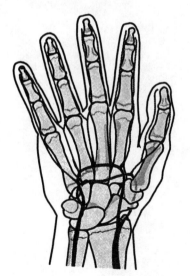

The major arterial vessels that flow to the hand are the radial and ulnar arteries. These, in turn, divide into the superficial planar arch and the deep palmar arch. The palmar metacarpal and common palmar digital arteries complete the smaller arterial system.
⬅

2
Observation of Hand Shapes

The shape of the hand is the broadest or most general category of observation in Chinese palmistry. In Chinese, it is called *shou xing zhi*. Observation of the shape of the hand provides an overview of the hand's general shape, size, skin texture, and color. The palms, flexure lines, fingers, and fingernails are all relatively independent aspects and are discussed individually in subsequent chapters. Each aspect has its own definitive qualities that can be analyzed and then synthesized with information gathered from other parts of the hand.

In Chinese medical palmistry, the hand is categorized into six general shapes. These are the primitive, square, bamboo, cone, (soup)spoon, and delicate hands.

1. Primitively shaped

Dorsal Digital Lines

This type of hand has the external appearance of being short and crooked. The finger knuckles are as thick and rough as the root of a tree. The dorsal digital lines are deep and disorderly, and the dorsal metacarpal veins are exposed and on the surface, while the skin color and luster are relatively deep. →

This type of hand indicates a good physical condition. Even if there is illness, it is slight. However, there is a tendency for nervousness, hypertension, and respiratory diseases.

2. Square-shaped

The square-shaped hand characteristically is straight and square. Its sinews and bones are thick and strong with the exception of the fingers. The wrist is also square-shaped. The dorsal digital creases are relatively light, *i.e.*, not very deep or prominent.

This hand shape shows good physical strength with full
vitality. Physical development is fairly good.
It is a vigorous and graceful hand shape.
In five phase palmistry, the square-shaped
hand is associated with earth.
Since the body is made from physical
matter or earth, a square-shaped hand is
a sign of a good physical constitution. ➜

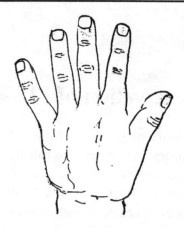

3. Bamboo-shaped

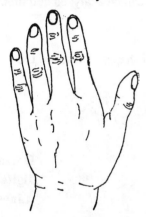

The external appearance of this hand shape is fairly long
and the joints are high. The dorsal digital creases are
obvious and the skin color is deep. The dorsal digital
tendons, hand muscles, and blood vessels are bulging.
⬅

This hand indicates a good intellect. However, the physical
strength is relatively weak due to excessive mental activity.
The respiratory, urological, and reproductive system
functions all tend to be weak. In five phase palmistry, this
hand shape pertains to fire.

4. Cone-shaped

With this shape, both the hand and fingers are
characteristically thin, long, soft, and slender. The fingertips are relatively pointed. The skin color tends to be pale
and the dorsal digital creases are light. The hand muscles
are soft and elastic, and the blue veins are unexposed.
➜

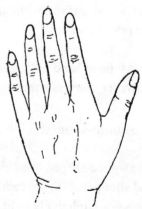

This hand shape shows an inclination to weak spleen and
stomach function with a tendency for digestive system
disease. On reaching middle and advanced age, there is a
tendency for arthritis or what is known in TCM as painful *bi* diseases.

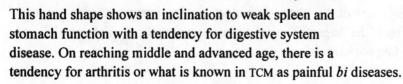

5. Spoon-shaped

This hand shape is usually seen in large or tall individuals. The sinews and bones are strong with thick, square fingers. However, the finger tips are unusual. Instead of tapering, the tips are thick and large, appearing similar to soupspoons. ➜

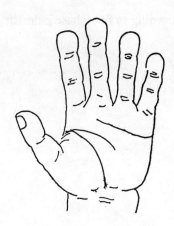

This shape of hand shows moderate health with a tendency for a quick temper. Hypertension and diabetes are likely, especially when thick, blue veins appear on the dorsal metacarpal surface.

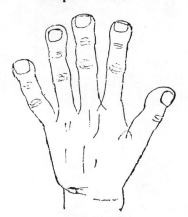

There is also another type of abnormal shape that is similar to the spoon shape. This is called a drumstick finger and needs to be differentiated. In this hand shape, the finger tip gradually increases in size and thickness after ther person has become ill. The digital root is relatively small. The palm is thinner and weaker. It is seen in primary heart disease, circulatory problems due to heart disease, and in the late stage of pulmonary tuberculosis. Drumstick fingers are also discussed under finger shapes. ⬅

6. Delicately shaped

In persons with this shape, the fingers and palm are thin and slightly crooked. The fingers are delicate with no strength and the fingertips are pointed. The skin color is a pale white and blue veins are relatively obvious. ➜
This hand indicates a condition of poor general health with a tendency to neurasthenia and timidity. There is also the tendency for respiratory disease, and urological and reproductive system functions are relatively weak.

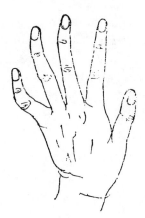

According to five phase palmistry, this hand shape pertains to water.

3
Observation of the Fingers

The fingers are the end points of the upper extremities. The qi and blood extend to this point and then return back to circulate within the body. According to Chinese medical palmistry, each of the five fingers reflects the condition of health at a different age in life. The thumb reflects the condition of health in childhood. The index finger reflects that of youth. The middle finger shows the condition of health in adult life. The ring finger reflects the health of the later period of adult life. And the small finger shows the condition of health in old age.

Observation of the fingers themselves can be divided into certain categories. These are their shape, length, strength, color, and the idiosyncracies of each individual finger.

Finger Shapes

There are five different finger shapes categorized in Chinese medical palmistry. They are square, spoon, cone, thin and long, and drumstick.

1. Square-shaped

The square-shaped finger looks like its name. It is square-shaped with blunt fingertips. This shape denotes basic good health. At times, it may show a tendency for neurasthenia and kidney or gallstones.

➜

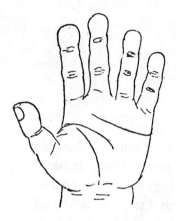

2. Spoon-shaped

The spoon-shaped finger also looks like its name since its tip looks like a soup spoon. This shape is indicative of an acidic constitution with a propensity for heart and cerebrovascular disease. It may also indicate diabetes. ←

3. Cone-shaped

The cone-shaped finger is round and long. The fingertip is pointed. The overall appearance is of a long cone. This shaped finger has a tendency for diseases of the chest or, in other words, illnesses below the neck and above the diaphragm. →

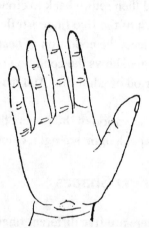

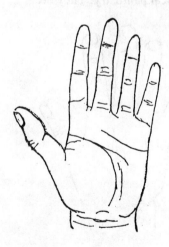

4. Thin & long-shaped

The thin and long-shaped finger is exactly as its name, thin and long. People whose fingers are this shape have an inclination for gastrointestinal diseases and for emotional depression. ←

5. Mixed shape

Mixed shape hands are those on which the five fingers
show various combinations of different finger shapes.
Individuals with this type of finger shape show an
especially strong resistance to disease and it is unusual for
them to become ill. ➜

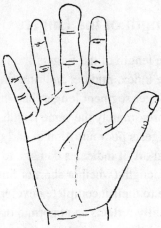

6. Drumstick-shaped

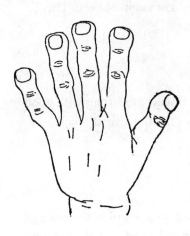

The drumstick shape is similar to
spoon-shaped fingers, yet the digital root is comparatively
small and the fingertips are thicker and larger. The tips
gradually increase in size with the condition of the disease.
The palm tends to be small, thin, and weak with drumstick
fingers. Fingers this shape usually indicate chronic respiratory
disease, such as late stage pulmonary tuberculosis, lung
cancer, pulmonary abscess, pulmonary/heart disease,
congenital heart disease, or circulatory system disease caused
by heart disease. In TCM terms, this shape finger indicates lung
qi depression and blockage or heart qi not reaching or
extending.
←

Whether the Fingers are Crooked or Straight

To determine whether the fingers are crooked or straight, one looks at the fingers when they are
adducted together. If the seams between the fingers is relatively large, this indicates that the
health at a certain age was relatively poor. This is usually due to the spleen/stomach debility. In
some individuals with hypertension, the fingers incline toward the thumb when extended.

Length of the Fingers

The length of the fingers should be straight and long. The thumb should be thick and strong. The index, middle, and ring fingers should be well arranged, with the middle finger one half of a finger segment longer than the index and ring finger. The index and ring fingers should be approximately the same length. If the index finger is excessively long or short, this usually suggests poor nutrition in early youth or frequent illness. If the ring finger is excessively long or short, it indicates damage to the viscera and bowels during adulthood. However, in infants, the length (whether short or long) of both the ring and index fingers is relatively insignificant due to their incomplete development. If the middle finger is excessively long or short, this usually reflects an abnormal or morbid state in adulthood. If the small finger is excessively long or short, it indicates a propensity for heart, spleen, and kidney disease in old age. This includes cerebrovascular disease and digestive system dysfunction.

Strength of the Fingers

The thumb and index finger are generally the strongest. If all five fingers are strong with good development, this indicates good health. If one finger is especially thin, this usually indicates poor health corresponding to the relevant period of age.

Color of the Fingers (skin and veins)

The observation of color includes the blood color and the blue veins. In particular, the color of the terminal segment of the fingers is important in assessing health and disease. The terminal segment of the fingers reflects the condition of the blood microcirculation. It is a good indication of the general condition of health.

The color of the fingertips should be red or ruddy. This shows good blood and qi circulation. Paleness shows a shortage of blood and qi, whereas a dark, purple color usually indicates blood stasis. Factors such as climate, temperature, work, and sudden emotional disturbance should all be taken into account when looking at the color of the fingers so as avoid jumping to an erroneous conclusion.

The superficial veins' best point of observation is at the interphalangeal creases on the palmar surface of the fingers. Normal individuals have faint, light blue veins on the surface. If the veins here are numerous or very obvious, this is considered abnormal.

Swollen Finger Joints

These are mostly seen in *bi* patterns. In this case, wind, cold, damp evils obstruct the network vessels of the joints resulting in inhibition of the qi and blood. If the joints are red and swollen, this is mostly due to damp heat. It may also be due to liver/kidney essence blood deficiency and vacuity with blood heat engendered internally. In terms of modern Western medicine, patients with swollen finger joints are usually suffering from arthritis, whether osteoarthritis or rheumatoid arthritis.

Individual Fingers

Each finger also has its own individual characteristics.

1. Thumb

The thumb is the most important among the five fingers. It shows the condition of one's congenital inheritance and intellectual function. Generally, the thumb should be full, long, and strong with phalanges of equal length. These are all signs of good health. An excessively strong thumb indicates a quick temper.

Conversely, a very thin, flat thumb signifies a poor constitution, nervousness, and lack of tenacity. A short thumb shows a lack of courage and a tendency to be emotional. A short thumb with a very stiff interphalangeal joint usually indicates hypertension, headache, and heart disease as well as apoplexy. And disordered or scattered distal finger creases show a tendency toward nervousness, headaches, and insomnia.

2. Index finger

The index finger should be strong with the three finger phalanges of equal length or gradually shortening from the proximal to the terminal phalanx. The finger should be straight and adduct tightly to the middle finger. This is a sign of proper liver and gallbladder function. If the proximal phalanx is excessively long, then the condition of health is relatively poor. If the middle phalanx is too thick, then the absorption of calcium is imbalanced. In that case there is a tendency for skeletal and dental problems early in life.

If the terminal phalanx is too short, this shows an inclination toward emotional and psychological illness. A thin and pale index finger indicates slightly poor liver and gallbladder function with a tendency to fatigue easily. A deviated fingertip with cracks and scattered lines on the knuckle creases and large finger knuckles indicates abnormal transformation and transportation function of the spleen and stomach. However, this dysfunction is usually due to liver and gallbladder imbalances.

3. Middle finger

The middle finger should be full, long, and strong with the lengths of the three phalanges about the same. It is the longest of all the five fingers and its linear shape should be straight without deviation. The knuckles should be supple, neither weak nor hard. All of these signs indicate good health with sufficient original qi.

If the finger is thin, small, weak, and pale, it indicates insufficient cardiovascular function or possibly anemia. A deviated fingertip with a phalanx showing a "leaking" seam indicates relatively weak heart and small intestine function. If the three phalanges are not symmetrical and the middle phalanx is especially long, this indicates insufficient energy and a lack of tenacity. It further shows that calcium metabolism is abnormal and thus there is a tendency for skeletal and dental disease. An excessively long middle finger denotes the propensity for internal damage by the seven affects.

4. Ring finger

This finger should be straight and strong, without deviation. The lengths of the phalanges should be equal, with the whole length of this finger reaching halfway to the middle finger's terminal phalanx. If this finger is excessively long, it is due to an imbalanced lifestyle. If the ring finger is too short, this usually indicates insufficiency of original qi. If this finger is thin, small, and pale, it shows weak kidney and reproductive system function.

The proximal phalanx finger knuckle of the ring finger indicates internal and reproductive ability. If the flexion creases are disorderly and scattered, this is a sign of a relatively poor physical condition. If this happens during pregnancy, calcium should be supplemented.

Creases on the palmar surface of the middle phalanx of the ring finger are called disease measurement creases. These creases increase and decrease along with the condition of health.

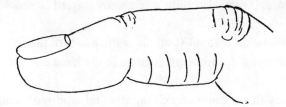

If the middle phalanx is excessively long, weak, and pale, it indicates that the absorption of calcium is relatively poor. This results in skeletal and dental weakness. If the terminal phalanx is deteriorated and shows a open leaking seam, then urological diseases tend to occur. It further shows a tendency toward neurasthenia and emotional depression. If the terminal phalanx is longer than one half of the middle finger's terminal phalanx (*i.e.*, is almost equal to the middle finger in length), this indicates a good primary physical constitution.

5. Small finger

The small finger should be straight and slender with phalanges of equal length. The length of this finger should be equal to the distal knuckle of the ring finger or slightly over this. These signs indicate proper functioning of the spleen and stomach and a good health condition. This finger is the basis for judging the condition of the digestive and reproductive systems. If it is thin and weak, this usually indicates poor digestion, malabsorption, diarrhea, or irregularity of the bowels. This is especially true if there is a deviated finger tip and a large open seam between the small and ring fingers. In addition, if this finger bends slightly, it indicates a small vital capacity. If the proximal phalanx's flexure creases appear disorderly or scattered, this indicates poor physical ability. If the small finger bends to the side with very dry skin on its palmar surface, this usually indicates incomplete digestion and malabsorption.

Other Signs Pertaining to Finger Observation

Have the patient stand erect with eyes closed and extend both hands flat with open fingers. A slight tremor is one sign of hyperthyroidism.

If all the fingertips are pale and feel icy cold, this indicates the possibility of chronic gastrointestinal disease. It may also show a tendency toward stomach cancer.

If the wrist hangs downward without strength or the joints of the fingers look similar to a bird's claw, this indicates atrophy due to nerve damage in the hand and forearm.

If the thumb and index finger cannot touch rapidly and repeatedly and the index finger mound is higher than the other mounds, this indicates the possibility of cerebral hemorrhage.

The Fingerprints

Fingerprints are the pattern made by the cutaneous ridges on the palmar surface of the terminal phalanges of each finger. They are fully developed at birth and never change throughout one's life. No two individuals have fingerprints exactly alike. In Chinese medical palmistry, there are three main types of fingerprints. These are whorl-shaped prints, loop-shaped prints, and arch-shaped prints.

1. Whorl-shaped prints

These manifest in two ways. One way is as concentric circles and the other is a spiral or whorl. These are considered yang fingerprints. ➜

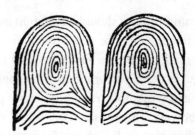

2. Loop-shaped prints

At each bottom of the left and right, there is an inverted Y-shaped print structure with ridge lines looping in three directions. Loops having such a three-sided fork opening toward the side of the small finger are called ulnar loops. If they open toward the side of the thumb, they are called radial loops. If these two types are intermixed, they are called double loops. These are considered yin fingerprints.

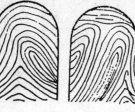

3. Arch-shaped prints

These refer to either high or low arches that cross the finger pad but do not fork into a three-sided Y shape. They are also considered yin fingerprints. ➡

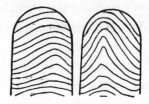

The ATD Angle

Except for the thumb, there is a Y-shaped, three-sided fork on the palmar surface of the palm at the base of each of the four fingers. Counting from the base of the index finger, these are called the A finger three fork, the B finger three fork, the C finger three fork, and the D finger three fork. There is also an inverted Y-shaped three fork near the wrist which is called the T three fork. ➡

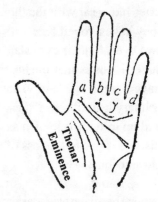

Normal Palm Distribution

If one links the A, T, and D three forks together by drawing a line from the T to A and T to D, an acute angle can be seen. The number of degrees in a normal (*i.e.*, undeformed) hand's ATD angle is below 40. If the ATD angle is above 40 degrees, this is considered abnormal. As mentioned above, the T three fork is the tip of the angle that decides this degree. The higher this Y-shaped three fork is, the larger the degree of the ATD angle will be. This is a very

important health index. For instance, most
patients with chromosomal disease have
a high Y-shaped three fork. ➡

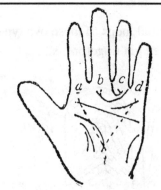

Typically, chromosomal diseases manifest with
conspicuously abnormal hand prints. If there
is an increase in the total number of whorl-shaped
prints with the number reaching 8-10 and if the
patient's body is short and she has primary amenorrhea
and failure to develop secondary sex characteristics,

Chromosomal Disease Palm Distribution

these signs and symptoms usually indicate primary ovarian insufficiency
syndrome or Turner's syndrome. This disease is due to the lack of one X chromosome.

If 1) the total number of whorl-shaped prints increase up
8-10, 2) the ATD angle is 60-70 degrees, 3) there is a
Simian crease on one or both hands, 4) the individual
cries like a cat with the thumb bending toward its back, 5)
they have a round face with a large distance between their
two eyes, 6) their eyes slant downwards, 7) there is
superfluous skin at the inner corner of the eyes, 8) they
have a small jaw, and 9) some individuals also have
primary heart disease, these signs and symptoms typically
add up to what is known as cat's cry syndrome. This
disease is due to the loss of the short arm of the fifth
chromosome. ➡

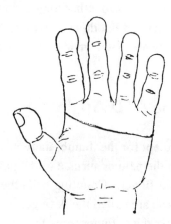

Simian Crease

When the fingerprints are mostly ulnar loops but the prints on the fourth and fifth fingers are
radial loops, the upside down T Y-shaped loop moves toward the center of the palm, and the
ATD angle is around 60-70 degrees, these signs are usually seen with a simian crease. Besides
this simian crease, such patients may also present with other characteristic signs. These include
an epicanthic fold, a low, flat root of the nose, a half-open mouth, a tongue that often sticks out,
low IQ, slow development, and a late start in sitting, standing, walking, and talking. These are
all signs usually seen in congenital Down's syndrome. This condition is due to an extra twenty-

first chromosome. This is one of the most common congenital abnormalities. On average, one in 600-800 individuals has this chromosomal abnormality.

All individuals with chromosomal deformity have abnormal handprints. Normal individuals have 46 chromosomes, which are matched into 23 pairs. Among them, 22 pairs are autosomes with the same shape and size. The other pair are the sex chromosomes. The congenital abnormalities described above are all due to chromosomal aberrations—either extra or fewer than normal chromosomes. In addition, many chromosomal syndromes are accompanied by characteristic changes in one's handprints. Although these may manifest in different ways, they all have certain things in common:

1) Simian crease
2) An upside down Y-shape T that moves toward the center of the palm, and an ATD angle that is larger than 60 degrees.
3) Increased curving prints
4) Increased whirling prints
5) Reverse loops on the ring and small fingers
6) Increased double loops

These characteristics are easy to recognize. They are different from normal handprints. They are especially significant as diagnostic markers since they appear before other characteristic signs and symptoms show, such as late development. Thus they can help establish an early diagnosis and lead to early treatment.

Other diseases besides chromosomal syndromes can also cause abnormal handprints. It has been discovered at a cancer research center that females who have a higher number of finger prints opening toward the right on their left hands have a greater chance of developing breast cancer.

Loop-shaped prints on all ten fingers and a simian crease indicate that some individuals within the patient's family will have a hereditary disease associated with decreased intelligence and slow development. Individuals with this type of hereditary disease also have a characteristic handprint. In this case, there will be only one flexure line on the small finger. Normally there are two. Patients with hereditary diseases, such as schizophrenia, epilepsy, diabetes, psoriasis, leprosy, and primary glaucoma, all exhibit similar handprint phenomena.

In addition, the fingerprints can point to other health problems, both currently existing and tendencies for the future. For instance, extremely clear fingerprints indicate the possibility of a lack of or damage to the bicuspid valve of the heart, while fingerprints with mainly whorl-shaped patterns indicate a tendency toward senile dementia.

4
Observation of the Fingernails

Anatomical Terms Pertaining to the Fingernails

The distal margin of the nail is called its far extremity. The proximal margin of the nail is called its near extremity. Implanted into a groove in the skin on the most proximal part of the nail is the nail root. The exposed part of the nail is called the nail body. The bulging skin covering the nail root and lateral sides is called the nail fold. The cuticle tissue that extends distally from the nail root is the eponychium. It partially covers the opaque crescent-shaped area at the near extremity called the lunula or small moon. The sunken furrow between the nail fold and the nail body is called the nail groove. Beneath the nail body is the nail bed.

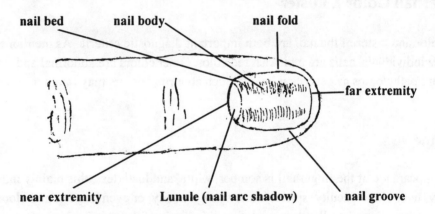

Main Points in Observing the Fingernails

Observing the nail is best done when the patient is in a quiet state. It is useless to observe the nails after the patient has carried heavy loads, if they are covered with dirt, or if they are wearing any type of nail polish. Practitioners should, therefore, keep a small bottle of nail polish remover handy so that female patients may remove their nail polish before the practitioner attempts to observe their nails.

TCM Theory Concerning the Fingernails

The fingernails are the surplus of the sinews, which in turn are governed by and connected to the liver and gallbladder. Therefore, by inspecting the fingernails one can determine pathological changes in the liver and gallbladder. However, the fingernails are mutually related to the entire body and all the viscera and bowels. Thus, an examination of the fingernails can reveal the state of the exuberance and decline of both righteous and evil qi in the whole body. Normal fingernails should be a pale red. They should be level, slippery, and lustrous. They should neither be too soft nor too brittle. When pressed and released, the color of the blood should quickly return underneath the nails. In that case, one can infer that the qi and blood are full and sufficient and that their transportation and movement are flowing and uninhibited. If the nails' color, shape, appearance, or strength is abnormal, this indicates some pathological change in the body.

Fingernail Color & Luster

The color and luster of the nail are both important diagnostic criteria. As mentioned above, a healthy individuals' nails are a pinkish red color. Other colors are abnormal and reflect different pathologies as described below. Such abnormal colors may range from pale white to black.

1. White

If the appearance of the fingernail is somber, white, and lusterless, this mainly indicates qi vacuity, liver blood vacuity, spleen/kidney yang vacuity, or even heart qi and blood insufficiency. In modern Western medicine, this is one of the classic signs of anemia. However, persons with pale, white nails may not have what modern Western medicine considers anemia but still be diagnosed by TCM practitioners as suffering from blood vacuity. Therefore, care should be taken in making this distinction.

If the fingernail is colored a lusterless, waxy, white, this indicates ulcerative bleeding or hookworm disease. In other words, it shows a chronic loss of blood. If the large part under the fingernail is a white color with the normally pink area decreased to only one small strip near the fingertip, this indicates the possibility of cirrhosis of the liver. A white nail that looks like frosted glass with its far extremity reddish brown indicates incomplete kidney function causing hyperagoturia.

A single white horizontal line crossing the nail is typically seen in arsenic and lead poisoning. However, this may also indicate Hodgkin's disease or pellagra (vitamin B deficiency). Two white lines crossing transversely on the nail often indicate a decrease of albumin in the blood. It is also seen in cases of hypoproteinemia due to chronic kidney disease. If there are dot-shaped or thread-like white speckles on the surface of the nail, this is usually due to some obstruction to nutrition and commonly indicates chronic liver disease, cirrhosis of the liver, or kidney disease. And a grayish white color on the fingernail can be a sign of late stage pulmonary tuberculosis and pulmonary heart disease.

Besides the above, it should to be noted that completely white colored nails may be congenital or may be associated with particular professions. In the elderly, white-speckled lumps or longitudinal stripes may appear periodically. This is a common change and may not be abnormal. However, tiny white speckles under the nail bed may indicate a lack of calcium, zinc, or parasitic disease. They may also be seen in individuals who are nervous, fatigued, or who have habitual constipation. Poisoning by various medicines or nicotine may also cause these white speckles to appear.

2. Yellow

In TCM, a bright yellow color mostly indicates damp heat smoldering and steaming. This is seen in cases with jaundice. In that case, a fresh yellow color shows a normal disease progression, while a dark, stagnant yellow is indicative of an ominous disease change.

According to modern Western medicine, when a yellow color appears on the fingernails, it typically indicates a liver dysfunction, such as jaundice due to hepatitis. However, it may also be seen in chronic hemorrhagic diseases. Other causes of yellow fingernails are hypothyroidism, nephrotic disease, hypervitaminosis A, and also fungal infections of the nails. High supplemental intake of betacarotene will also cause yellowing of the fingernails. Betacarotene is nontoxic. Excessive Vitamin A is toxic. Therefore, care should be taken in assessing whether patients with yellow fingernails have taken large doses of Vitamin A or betacarotene.

When the fingernail is both yellow and thick and also has a large curving angle, grows slowly (less than 0.2mm per week), and there is thoracic cavity infiltration and primary lymphedema, all these signs are referred to as yellow nail syndrome.

A yellow, copper-colored fingernail that has the appearance of having been hammered is caused by autoimmune baldness disease, of which little is known. Its symptoms are partial or complete baldness. A yellow color appearing around the fingertip indicates the need to be cautious of melanoma. Longterm use of tetracycline may also cause yellow nails. In the elderly, light yellow nails may be due to the normal degeneration of aging. In addition, long-term smoking can also cause a yellowing of fingernails due to staining by tars from the tobacco. These last causes are not considered abnormal.

3. Red

In terms of TCM pattern discrimination, red indicates heat. Thus red nails mainly indicate pathological heat. This may be either qi heat or blood heat. If the nails are light red, this is vacuity heat. If the nails are deep red, this is replete heat. If the nails are red with a purplish appearance, this indicates heat and simultaneous toxins. However, *bi* patterns with serious wind affecting the joints may also manifest this color. A dark purplish red color indicates blood stasis. This may be seen in cases of phlegm fire wind heat obstructing the chest and lungs, qi and blood depression and blockage, etc. Red spots in the nails tend to indicate blood stasis or bleeding due to heat. These may be either brownish red, purplish red, or simply red.

In terms of modern Western medicine, red areas in the nail may be indicative of a number of different diseases. A bright red area near the nail root and a light red color over the rest of the fingernail can be seen in cough and hemoptysis. If these colors show in the opposite places, it may indicate chronic kidney disease. A bright red color over the whole nail is a sign of early stage pulmonary tuberculosis and intestinal tuberculosis. If, on pressing and releasing the nail, the color returns rapidly, then the disease is light. If the color returns slowly, the disease is chronic.

A red freckle or red strip under the fingernail indicates capillary bleeding. It may be due to hypertension, dermatosis, heart infection, or some latent disease. Red freckles around the fingernail indicate the possibility of dermatomyositis or systemic lupus erythematosus (SLE). A transverse red stripe on the near extremity indicates there is inflammation of the gastrointestinal tract, cardiac valve prolapse, or atrioventricular septum defect. And a deep red color that does not change after the nail is pressed indicates inflammation in certain viscera.

4. Purple

A purple color manifesting on a fingernail is usually a sign of heart and blood disease. From a modern Western medical point of view, it indicates a lack of oxygen or an abnormal component part in the blood. If the nails are sometimes purple and pale white, this may indicate Raynaud's disease. In TCM, the purple color typically indicates stagnation and stasis.

5. Indigo blue

An indigo blue nail may appear in different conditions. During an acute abdominal episode, fainting, or what TCM refers to as cold inversion of the four limbs, the fingernails may suddenly become indigo blue. In pregnancy, a continuous indigo blue color of the nails may indicate a dead fetus. An indigo blue nail with green stasis speckles can indicate poisoning or early stage cancer. An indigo blue, purplish nail can often be seen in primary heart disease, lobar pneumonia, or severe pulmonary emphysema. In all these cases, the indigo blue color denotes stasis and stagnation.

6. Green

A green color, either on a part or on the whole nail, is usually related to chronic contact with soaps and detergents. It may also be caused by pyocyanic infection or green aspergillus.

7. Blue

A blue color on the fingernail can be seen in diphtheria, lobar pneumonia, acute infectious diseases of the intestinal tract, and obstruction in the esophagus by a foreign body. Wilson's disease, which is a hepatolenticular, copper metabolism disorder, can also cause blue fingernails. Enterogenous cyanosis (caused by ingesting spoiled vegetables) as well as nitrite poisoning can cause normal ferrous hemoglobin to oxidize or ferric hemoglobin to lose its ability to transport oxygen and thus cause tissue hypoxemia. This manifests as cyanosis of the skin and hence blue fingernails also occur.

Certain substances, such as sulphur, nitrite atebrin, and primaquine, can also cause blue fingernails. If the root shows a blue crescent shape, this indicates a damaged circulatory system, *i.e.*, heart disease or Raynaud's disease. Blue fingernails may also be related to rheumatoid arthritis (RA) or autoimmune disease, such as SLE or Cazebaves' lupus.

Generally in TCM, the blue color is associated with cold patterns. However, it may also be associated with blood stasis. In enduring disease, if the nails are blue and the hands and feet are also blue or blue-green, this indicates liver expiry and the patient's prognosis is not good.

8. Gray

The appearance of a gray color on the nail can be seen in various systemic diseases such as myxedema, rheumatoid arthritis, or hemiplegia. Poor nutrition can cause fingernail thickening or atrophy together with pigmentation changes, for example, the gray color. If the near extremity shows a gray, wavy shape, this can indicate glaucoma.

Greyish-brown colored nails in TCM often are seen with liver depression and qi stagnation.

9. Black

A black colored fingernail can be due to trauma to the fingertip itself causing bleeding under the injured nail. Initially the color is a purplish red and gradually changes to a purplish black color. TCM describes this as local blood stasis due to the channels and network vessels having been damaged. In this case, this does not mean that there is blood stasis internally. However, Ma Zhong-xue's *Zhong Guo Yi Xue Zhen Fa Da Quan (Great Collection of Chinese Medicine Diagnostic Techniques)* says, "If the fingernail is black, this is mainly blood stasis and pain with dead blood congealing internally." Thus a blackish fingernail may be a sign of blood stasis accumulating internally if not due to local trauma of the nail.

Further, if the nail is a withered black color, this is an ominous sign. If this manifests after an enduring disease, it mostly pertains to kidney expiry. If the nails are black and at the same time there is inversion of the limbs (*i.e.*, chill), counterflow vomiting, and the cheeks are darkish and green-blue, this also signals an ominous turn in a disease.

Increased myelin in the nail bed matrix and the deposition of the heavy metal silver can also cause brownish-black nails. A blackish-blue color under or around the marginal structure of the fingernail may indicate paronychia caused by pyogenic infection. In chronic renal failure, an obvious black color is often seen at the far extremity of the fingernail. Vitamin B_{12} deficiency, adrenocortical failure, gastrointestinal polyp syndrome, or chronic contact with coal tar can all manifest as grayish-black fingernails.

There are two other nail color manifestations that relate to black nails. All black or brown nails or speckled shapes particularly on the thumb or great toe, especially if the surrounding tissue also shows a brown or black color, indicate the possibility of a malignant tumor, *i.e.*, melanoma. A number of black lines appearing in the nail root, usually growing to the middle of the fingernail, also indicate the development of cancer in the body. In such cases, further testing is essential in order to establish a definite diagnosis and thus commence timely treatment.

Fingernail Thickness & Resilience

The resilience of the nail is another aspect that should be assessed in the medical analysis of the nails. Generally, springy, resilient nails are a sign of good health. Hard, brittle nails are commonly due to nutritional problems. Soft, thin nails represent both lack of energy and lack of calcium. This type of nail is often seen in people who are nervous or suffer from chronic wasting or consumptive disease.

In TCM, dry, withered nails mostly indicate liver heat. These may also be seen in case of heart yin insufficiency, liver blood deficiency and vacuity, and inhibition of the transportation of blood. If the nails are withered like fish scales, this mostly pertains to kidney qi insufficiency. It may also be due to loss of spleen fortification and transportation with water dampness flooding and spilling. Severe wind and great toxins may also cause the nails to be withered and shrunken.

Thin, brittle nails are, without exception, due to qi and blood deficiency and vacuity and essence blood not spreading to its proper place. They may also be seen in pestilential diseases and fingernail *xian* or tinea.

Coarse, old, thick nails may be due to qi vacuity and blood dryness engendering wind, immersion and soaking in water dampness, or external invasion of damp toxins.

Lunulae

The crescent shapes at the base or near extremity of the nail are called the lunulae. They are also known as the health circle or nail arc shadow. The lunula of the thumb is the largest. Normally, the lunula on the thumb should be one-fifth of the length of the nail. The lunulae then grow in order of the index, middle, ring, and finally the small finger. These lunulae are believed to indicate the general physical condition, whether weak or strong, and especially the condition of the cardiovascular system. If all five fingers have lunulae and the lunulae are normally proportioned, this is a sign of good health. Excessively large and disproportionate lunulae commonly indicate hypertension and apoplexy. Absent lunulae indicate anemia, neurasthenia, hypotension or weak physical strength. After a stroke, the lunulae can become obscured, and small or obscure lunulae may indicate a tendency for cerebomalacia, acute pneumonia, asthma, gout, and gastrointestinal disease, including gastroduodenal ulcer. In summary, excessively large, small, absent, or obscure lunulae are considered abnormal. This is why they are called "health circles."

In particular, the famous TCM oncology specialist, Sun Bing-yan, in his book *The Prevention & Treatment of Cancer* published in partial translation by Offete Enterprises of San Mateo, CA, refers to the lunulae as the first of his "three marks" in predicting cancer. According to Dr. Sun, the lunulae show the amount of righteous yang qi or heat in the body. People with normal sized lunulae have a normal amount of righteous heat derived prenatally from the kidneys and postnatally from the spleen/stomach. People with smaller than normal lunulae therefore tend to suffer from weak spleen/stomach function and the accumulation of evil yin, such as depressive dampness. Conversely, people with larger than normal lunulae tend to suffer from yang repletion diseases.

As mentioned above, the lunulae are largest and most obvious on the thumb and each successive finger's lunula tends to be a little smaller. Therefore, in assessing the lunulae, an easy method is to count how many lunulae are present. Thus a person may be said to have ten lunulae, eight lunulae, six lunulae, an so on. Usually the size of the lunulae is symmetrical on both hands.

As a practical extension of this, people with smaller and fewer lunulae should avoid eating cold and raw foods and drinking cold liquids with meals. They should eat mostly neutral and warm foods at room temperature or warm. And they should eat warming spices, such as ginger, cardamon, and cinnamon. Further, when ill, even if they have damp heat or counterflowing yang, such people should not be given too many cool, cold medicinals and should be routinely given warm, spleen-fortifying, qi-boosting medicinals.

Conversely, patients who have larger than usual lunulae appearing on all ten nails should not eat much in the way of hot, spicy food. Nor should they drink alcohol or eat fatty foods or red meat. Rather, they should eat more cooling vegetables, more raw food, and should generally stick to what Chinese medicine refers to as a clear, bland diet. (For further information on Chinese dietary therapy and a clear, bland diet, see Bob Flaws' *Arisal of the Clear, A Simple Guide to Healthy Eating According to Traditional Chinese Medicine*, Blue Poppy Press, Boulder, CO).

According to Sun Bing-yan, a person's lunulae tend to be similar to their parents'. If the parents have few or small lunulae, so also will the children. But if the parents have all their lunulae and they are also larger than usual, then the children will also tend to have ten large lunulae. This suggests and Dr. Sun believes that the lunulae are, therefore, a very good indication for the assessment of constitutional vitality or what TCM refers to as one's former heaven or prenatal endowment. However, according to Dr. Sun, the size of these lunulae can change over time, reflecting either the progression or regression of the patient's condition.

Abnormal Fingernails

Fingernail abnormalities include abnormalities in fingernail shape, texture, and color and are important clues to particular diseases as well as to health tendencies.

Abnormal Nail Shapes

1. Grooves

Recessed transverse grooves or dips on the body of the nail show that the individual has had some type of previous health problem. This may have been an emotional disturbance or a nutritional imbalance.

Because the length of time it takes for the nail to grow is known (between 130-180 days), the time of the illness or stress corresponds to the number of days it has taken for the grooved region to grow to its present position on the surface of the nail. The two diagrams below show examples of grooves indicating diseases or stresses affecting nail growth occurring 50-70 days ago and 30-50 days ago.

Nail body with recessed groove

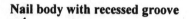

Illness 50-70 days ago   **Illness 30-50 days ago**

Individuals with more than one recessed nail groove usually have an intestinal parasitic condition and/or chronically weak intestinal function. If the recessed groove occurs on the thumb, the essence spirit is low. If it occurs on the index finger, this usually indicates a tendency toward skin diseases. If this groove is on the middle fingernail, it usually indicates the loss of muscular strength. On the ring finger, this groove shows a propensity for eye disease and bronchitis or respiratory disease. If it occurs on the small finger, laryngopharyngitis, neuralgia, or gallbladder disease may be indicated.

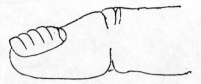

Nail body with traces of recessed groove

2. Distortions

Up-turned nails are often seen in individuals with spinal cord disease or alcoholism. They are also seen in arthritis. According to Ma Zhong-xue, what are called *fan jia* or concave nails mostly indicate liver blood insufficiency. They may also pertain to qi and blood stagnation and stasis. Down-turned nails, in other words, nails that are elongated and curve down like an eagle's talon or have an uneven nail body are usually seen among individuals with cardiovascular disease, qi stagnation, blood stasis, wind *bi*, sinew contraction, or calcium deficiency.

Nail turned down

Nail turned up

3. Shapes

A. Short & square

A short, square fingernail usually reflects an impatient disposition that can lead to heart disease, especially if the individual has small or absent lunulae. **(See figures on next page)**

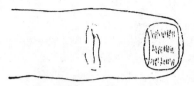

Short, square fingernail

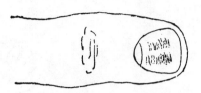

Triangular fingernail

B. Triangular

A triangular-shaped fingernail in which the tip of the nail is large and the root is small often appears among individuals with cerebrospinal and paralytic diseases. If the nail color is pale white or dark yellow, it means these diseases are presently occurring.

C. Atrophy

Nail body atrophy is usually seen among
individuals with dystrophy
or nervousness. ➜

D. Short & wide

A nail body that is short and wide indicates a relatively weak heart and a tendency toward numbness as well as diseases affecting the abdomen, low back, and lower part of the body.

E. Level & inlaid

If the nail tip is level and inlaid into the flesh, this
indicates a tendency for neuralgia and arthritis.
In females, there is a tendency for diseases of the
uterus and ovaries. If the nail body lacks
color and luster, infertility may be indicated. ➜

Nail body short & wide or inlaid into flesh

F. Olive-shaped

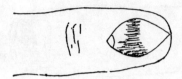

When the nail body is small at the near and far extremities and large in the middle, this is called an olive-shaped nail. This shape indicates an unsound or incomplete cardiovascular system or tendency toward spinal cord disease.

G. Thin, weak middle with creases

Creases in the nail body with a very thin, weak middle are due to hookworm disease. It also shows a nutritional deficiency of calcium and anemia. ➜

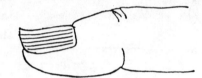

H. High center with curved down extremities

When the middle of the nail body is high and the two extremities curve down, it indicates an inclination for respiratory diseases—usually asthma, pulmonary tuberculosis, and pleurisy. This type of nail body is most significant when it happens more or less to all ten fingernails. ➜

I. Tube-shaped

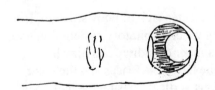

If the nail body is attached to the fingertip in a tube-like shape, tumorous disease may be indicated.

43

J. Flat

A nail body that is level with no curve similar to a flat sheet sticking to the finger tip indicates a very low resistance to disease. The individual is physically weak with frequent illnesses. ➜

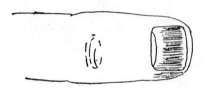

K. Fan-shaped

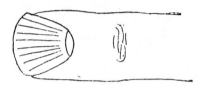

A fan-like or shell-shaped nail body where the far extremity is wide and the near extremity is narrow indicates nervousness and insufficient physical strength. It further shows an inclination for apoplexy, including cerebrovascular accident, as well for spinal cord disease. ⬅

L. Brittle with vertical lines

A brittle nail body surface with vertical lines displays a tendency for heart failure and skin diseases due to weak skin function. If the thumbnail has more vertical lines than the other fingernails, this indicates peculiar dietary habits that may induce disease. ➜

M. Long

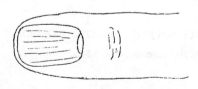

A long nail body indicates lack of body strength. It usually occurs with weak respiratory system function, although a small number of individuals may be symptom free. If the length increases and the color darkens with obvious vertical lines on the nail body surface, this increases the possibility of respiratory system disease.

N. Long & narrow

A long, narrow nail body shape is usually abnormal. A skeletal disease or especially a spinal cord pathology is indicated if the nail color is a light white or dark color. This nail indicates a tendency toward emotional depression. In females, there may be emotional disturbance or agitated viscera. ➡

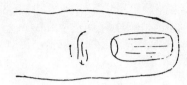

O. Very deep, straight grooves

If the nail body surface has very deep, straight grooves (different from vertical lines), this indicates poor nutrition or excessive work. They may also be seen in neurasthenia or weak respiratory system function. ➡

Falling Fingernails

If the nails fall off, this is mostly due to qi and blood insufficiency. If liver channel blood dryness is severe, this may also result in the nails falling off. Pyogenic infection underneath the fingernails may also make the nails fall off. This is called *dai zhi*, displaced fingers and *zao zhi*, rotten fingers. In this case, there are exuberant heat toxins blocking. Hence the qi is astringed and not free-flowing. In addition, pestilential wind may also cause the fingernails to fall off.

5
Observation of the Palm

The palm of the hand also has its very important story to tell about the health or disease of the individual. In fact, the palm is so important an area in the reading of the hand that, in English, the entire art of prognostication by reading the hand is simply known as palmistry.

Likewise, observing the palm is an important part of the overall assessment of the hand in Chinese medical palmistry. Palm observation includes the shape of the palm, abnormal appearances of the palm, abnormal palm colors, the thickness of the palm, the palm's relative moisture or dryness, the veins visible in the palm, and, in particular, the flexure lines on the palm.

This chapter covers the overall shape of the palm, abnormal appearances of the palm, abnormal palm colors, the thickness of the palm, the relative moistness or dryness of the palm, and a very brief, general discussion of the veins visible in the palm. The flexure lines or creases in the palm are dealt with in the next chapter.

Palm Shapes

There are several different shapes of palms categorized in Chinese medical palmistry. Generally, they can be divided into four types. These are the round, square, spoon, and rectangular shapes.

1. Round palm

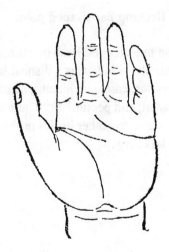

Most individuals with a round-shaped palm are healthy, energetic, tenacious, extroverted, and optimistic. They seldom have emotional problems. ➡

2. Square palm

Individuals with square-shaped palms generally have
good health and are serious and scrupulous in their
actions. They also tend to have a stubborn disposition.
However, as they age, there is a tendency toward
heart and cerebrovascular disease. ➡

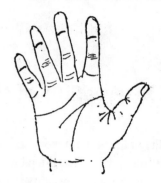

3. Spoon-shaped palm

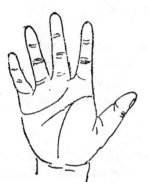

Individuals with spoon-shaped palms usually have a
large, thick wrist as well as comparatively large, thick
knuckles. They typically have an optimistic disposition,
good physical strength, and confidence. However, if
they do not control their drinking and smoking, they
tend to age prematurely. They are often fidgety and may
suffer from low back pain. This is especially the case in
individuals with large, thick wrists.

 ⬅

4. Rectangular-shaped palm

The muscles and flesh on palms of this shape are thin.
This shape indicates a disposition that is inward,
nervous, cautious, intense, sensitive, very emotional,
fearful, and pessimistic. There is a tendency toward
amnesia and other health problems. They tend not
to be energetic. ➡

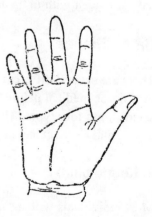

Abnormal Palm Appearances

1. Dry, wrinkled skin

Dry, wrinkled skin, similar to that seen on the hands of a laundry person, is usually a sign of acute stomach and intestinal tract disease with severe, frequent diarrhea and vomiting.

2. Flat, atrophic palms

Some people's palms may manifest severe muscular atrophy with a loss of their original shape. This can especially be seen in the area of the thenar and hypothenar eminences, making the palm look flat like a monkey's hand. Such a palm may indicate hand and arm injury and inflammation.

3. Edema of the palms

Water swelling of the palm and fingers with numbness indicate the possibility of heart disease.

4. Widening & thickening of the palm

If the whole palm becomes wider and thicker with short, thick fingers and the cheek, frontal, and mandible bones all protrude, these are signs seen in adult brain hypophysis tumor.

5. Blisters on the palm

Blisters on the skin of the palm, a peeling palm, or an extremely itchy palm usually indicate palmar tinea. This is a fungal condition of the palm similar to roundworm. In Chinese medicine it is called *shou xian*. TCM dermatology identifies three varieties of this condition: the blistery type, the erosive type (like athlete's foot of the palm and fingerwebs), and the squamous cornification type. The blister type is associated with evil wind and dampness. There erosive type is associated with dampness and heat. And the squamous cornification type is associated with blood vacuity and dryness engendering wind.

6. Dry, wrinkled skin on the back of the hand

Dry, wrinkled skin on the dorsal or back side of the hand with stiff finger joints and cold hands all year around are symptoms of what in Traditional Chinese Medicine is called hand and foot icy cold disease. This is usually seen among the old and infirm. If such symptoms occur irregularly and are accompanied by intolerable pain, a bluish-black facial color, and cold body sweats followed by a return to normal, these are signs usually seen in roundworm disease or ascariasis.

Abnormal Palm Colors

The color of a normal palm is a light red or pinkish red with a shiny, smooth texture. Normal palms are also springy and full of strength. If the color appears either darker or lighter than normal, this may indicate that the condition of one's health is abnormal.

1. Pale white

A palm appearing pale white in color indicates anemia or possibly occult bleeding. If the palm looks white, this usually indicates lung disease or inflammation in the body.

2. Blue

A blue palm usually indicates intestinal obstruction.

3. Green

A palm with a dark green color usually indicates obstruction in the circulation of the blood. A greenish palm that is not dark may indicate anemia or spleen/stomach disease.

4. Yellow

A sallow yellow palm usually indicates chronic disease. This is because chronic disease typically affects the spleen and stomach. Yellow is the color of earth and the spleen and stomach pertain to earth. In this case, the spleen and stomach are vacuous and weak. A palm with a bright, golden yellow color is often seen in liver disease accompanied by jaundice. In this case, there is liver/gallbladder damp heat. If the palm skin grows thicker, stiffer, and is dry with a light yellow, shiny, smooth surface, this is called palm calcar keratosis. This is a hereditary condition and usually occurs during infancy. A palm that looks yellowish brown and has no sheen indicates the possibility of cancer.

5. Red

A palm with red, net-like capillaries often appears with Vitamin C deficiency. If the whole palm is covered with dark red or purple spots, this is usually seen in liver disease. When the skin on the surface of the palm and especially on the thenar and hypothenar eminences and the fingertips appears congested red, this is commonly due to cirrhosis of the liver or cancer of the liver. A palm that first appears red and gradually changes to a dark purple is usually a sign of heart disease. It is an indication that the disease is worsening. An excessively red palm indicates a tendency for apoplexy. If the whole palm of a hypertensive patient appears black like tea, this is a forewarning of cerebral hemorrhage. If the skin of a red palm is as soft and smooth as satin, this indicates a tendency toward rheumatic fever.

In general in Chinese medicine, red indicates the presence of heat. However, there are a number of sources and types of heat according to TCM and thus there can be various shades of red associated with these types of heat. As the red becomes darker, this indicates that heat is being complicated by stagnation and stasis.

6. Purple

When the subcutaneous tissue of the palm shows prune-colored purple, it indicates serious infectious shock.

7. Grey

Thin cigarette-ash like spots on the palm of the hand are a sign of heart disease in a heavy smoker.

8. Black

A palm that looks black is often seen in kidney disease. If the central part of the palm looks brownish-black, this often indicates gastrointestinal diseases. A dark purple or black color appearing from the wrist to the hypothenar eminence is a sign of low back disease due to wind. The same kind of color may also appear on the medial side of the foot and ankle. ➜

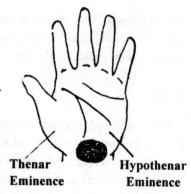

Thenar Eminence   **Hypothenar Eminence**

Thickness of the Palm

Individuals with a strong, thick palm tend to be very energetic. A soft, thin palm indicates weakness with a tendency to become ill. A fat yet weak, atonic palm also indicates a lack of qi. A stiff palm indicates lack of flexibility. A thin, hard palm indicates an unsound digestive system.

If the hypothenar eminence muscle and the muscles at the edge of the small finger are recessed and the skin has no sheen, it is usually due to the shortage of body fluids. This is often seen in chronic diarrhea and dysentery.

In general in TCM, a strong, robust physical shape is indicative of sufficient qi and blood. People who are not just robust but are beefy tend to be even replete. Conversely a thin, weak physical shape suggests insufficiency and vacuity of qi and blood. However, if the flesh is atonic and soft, even though it may be thick, this suggests spleen qi vacuity with accumulation of dampness.

All this is because the spleen rules the flesh and muscles and the roundness and fleshiness of the physique is due to the nourishment derived by the function of the spleen and stomach and also the spleen's ability to transport and transform body fluids. Because the spleen is known as the postnatal or latter heaven root of qi and blood production, assessing a person's flesh and muscle can tell a lot about their general energy level, gastrointestinal function, and resistance to disease.

Moisture & Dryness of the Palm

Dryness of the skin of the palm may be due either to external or internal factors. External factors include reactions to chemicals, reagents, and germs. For instance, dry skin on the palm may be due to repeated exposure to certain chemicals at work. Internally, some people are born with constitutionally dry skin, while others are more sensitive to cold.

In TCM, because the moisture of the skin is associated with the nourishing function of the blood and because the blood in women is easily damaged by menstruation, pregnancy and birthing, and lactation, often women have drier skin than men. The decline in blood production associated with aging is also the reason why the elderly have drier skin than the young. In addition, when it is cold, the blood vessels contract and the hands become dry due to a decrease of sweat secretion. This is why some people's hands chap in the winter or become abnormally dry when exposed to cold.

As for overly moist palms, an anxious state of mind may cause reactions in the nervous system that increases sweat secretion to the point of watery hands. It is also possible for the palms to be abnormally moist if one's spleen function is weak. In this case, the spleen fails to transport and transform water fluids, which then accumulate in the flesh and make it overly moist. This type of abnormally moist palms usually occurs in people whose skin color is pale white and whose palms are fat and atonic.

Veins

The veins in the palms may sometimes be more than usually obvious. They are so shallow that they may be seen between the finger knuckles. This usually indicates old fecal matter in the large intestine caused by heat and dryness. Individuals with this sign typically have habitual constipation or hemorrhoids. If the habitual constipation is corrected and the bowel movements are once again complete, these veins can become lighter and gradually disappear. Any hemorrhoidal bleeding will also then be resolved.

Retroversion of the uterus may also be observed through the veins on the palm of the hand. On female patients with backache during the menstrual period, fatigue, abdominal distension and pain, a light green color along with a green blood vessel will be seen on the palm. This vessel occurs at the radial side of the so-called earth crease on the proximal section of the thenar eminence on the right hand. ➜

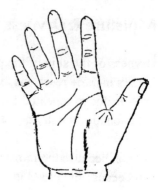

Lines

In Chinese, the lines on the palm are called *shou xian*, hand lines or routes. As we will see below, the lines in the palm have a very close relationship with health. Each line or crease in the hand says something about a particular flow of qi. Thus, different line shapes and the locations in which they appear indicate different health and disease conditions. These are discussed in detail in the following chapter. Below, however, are the definitions and illustrations of the main shapes of lines one finds in the palm and some general indications.

Characteristic shapes of lines in the palm

1. Star-shaped lines

This shape is comprised of 3 or 4 short lines and appears as a star. ➜

Star-shaped lines tend to indicate a spasmodic action or occurrence related to the organs or functions associated with where they appear in the palm. If they occur at the termination of a line, they typically show a sudden drain on the associated organ or function or a sudden stoppage in the flow of qi associated with this line.

2. Cross-shaped lines

This shape is comprised of two short lines in a criss cross pattern. ➜

Cross-shaped lines also indicate some spasmodic or obstructed flow of qi.

3. Island-shaped lines

This describes an island-like shape in a line made
when it separates into two lines, which then reform
somewhere further on. ➜

Island-shaped lines show division in the flow of qi of the associated line. The fact that the lines
rejoin shows that the condition is episodic and limited in duration. For instance, they may be
associated with a traumatic accident, a period of stress, or a self-limiting infectious disease.

4. Chain-shaped lines

This shape describes a line that is made up of many
islands or parallel striations rather than a single,
distinct crease. ➜

Chain-shaped lines show habitual inconstancy or fracturing in the qi flow of the associated
organ or functions with which the line is associated. Terence Dukes says that this is due to too
much fire within that flow of qi, thus causing the flow to be dispersed and erratic. From a
Western medical point of view, chain-shaped lines reveal malfunction of the neural stimuli
required by the organs or functions with which such lines correspond.

5. Well-shaped lines

In this case, four straight lines intersect to form
something that in English is called the pound sign.
It is called in the well shape in Chinese palmistry
because the Chinese character for well is written this
way. In Western palmistry, these shaped lines are
often referred to as a guille. ➜

Well-shaped lines show debilitation in the organs or functions associated with the area in which
they appear.

6
Observation of the Mounds & Lines

As mentioned in the introduction, Chinese five phase palmistry is based, at least in part, on Ayurvedic and Buddhist palmistry. Therefore, it is not altogether dissimilar to Western palmistry. In Western palmistry there is the concept of the four elements. The five phases (*wu xing*) in the Chinese system are basically analogous. The five phases as used in Chinese medicine and the system of medical palmistry presented herein are wood, fire, earth, metal, and water. In Chinese medicine, the organs of the body are divided into viscera (*zang*) and bowels (*fu*). Each viscus, which is yin, is paired with a bowel, which is yang, and each such viscus and bowel pair in the body is related to one of these five phases. In addition, the various functions and tissues associated in Chinese medicine with each viscus or bowel are also associated with the phase of that organ or bowel. Thus each phase in the body manifests in corresponding organs, physiological and pathophysiological functions, tissues, and righteous (*i.e.*, healthy) and evil (*i.e.*, pathological) substances.

For example, the spleen and stomach are associated with the earth phase and are the root of qi and blood transformation and engenderment. The spleen and stomach also rule digestion, which is the process by which qi and blood are produced and engendered. Further, the spleen and stomach govern the muscles and flesh, giving the body its healthy, rounded shape and empowering the muscles' strength and function of movement. Thus the earth phase as it manifests in the body is associated with digestion, abundant qi and blood, and the physical shape and strength of the body.

According to this system, each of the major mounds or mounts of the hand (*shou qiu*) are related to one of the five stars in turn correlated to the five phases or an associated Chinese cosmological concept. Thus in this system, there are two fire (*huo*) star mounds, an earth (*tu*) and a soil (*di*) mound, mounds corresponding to the sun (*tai yang*) and moon (*tai yin*) as well as mounds corresponding to wood (*mu*), metal (*jin*), and water (*shui*) stars. In addition, five phase palmistry pays great attention to the major and minor flexure creases or lines of the palm (*shou xian*). There are also discussions of more than a dozen lines and numerous abnormalities of their shapes, each with its own medical reading. These lines or creases are also each associated with one of the five phases.

Any landmark on the palm associated with a particular phase may reflect on any viscus, tissue, or function associated with that phase through Chinese five phase theory. In addition, the medical readings of these areas and lines are unique in the literature on palmistry in that they are based not only on the theory of systematic correspondence but also on modern Chinese clinical observations. ➜

The Five Phase Mounds on the Palm

1. Wood star mound

Location: The mound at the root of the index finger. This is the same location as the mound of Jupiter in Western palmistry.

Bodily correspondence: This area corresponds to the condition of the heart and liver. The liver is the viscus associated with the wood phase. ➜

Indications: If this mound is unusually elevated and there are scattered lines in this area, this indicates a tendency toward cerebrovascular and heart disease.

Explanation: A mound that is larger than usual indicates repletion or excess in the viscus or function with which it is associated. When replete, as in the case of liver yang hyperactivity, liver fire ascending upward, or internal stirring of liver wind, this may cause hypertension and apoplexy, including stroke. Because liver/wood is the mother of heart/fire according to the *sheng* or engenderment cycle of Chinese five phase theory, repletion in the mother can be passed on to the child. This is why repletion in the liver can not only affect the liver but also the entire cardiovascular system, causing both heart disease and cerebrovascular accident (CVA).

If a line arises from the human or proximal transverse crease and extends into the seam between the index and middle fingers, cutting the heaven or distal transverse crease under the root of the small finger, it indicates a tendency toward gastrointestinal disease. In TCM terms, this is due to the liver invading the spleen and stomach. ➜

2. Earth star mound

Location: The mound at the root of the middle finger. This is the same location as the mound of Saturn in Western palmistry.

Bodily correspondence: This area corresponds to the function of cardiovascular system.

Indications: Bulging and scattered lines in this area suggest a tendency toward nervous system disease, hemorrhoids, ear and tooth disease, and paralysis.

If, at the upper part of the distal transverse crease, there is a line extending straight up to the finger flexure line at the root of the middle finger and this line is cut by short, ➜ transverse lines one after the other, this usually indicates a weak physical condition.

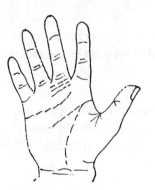

If the earth mound and the area near the root of the middle finger are crossed transversely by many lines, this usually indicates disease of the chest area. ⬅

A star-shaped line on the earth mound indicates a

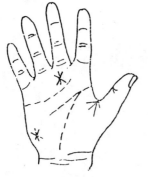

tendency for hypertension at a certain age. If there is also a star-shaped line on the moon mound, this increases the possibility of cerebrovascular accident. In this case, preventative measures should be taken before such an event occurs when the patient still feels otherwise healthy. ←

3. Sun mound

Location: The mound at the root of the ring finger. This is the same location as the mound of the Sun in Western palmistry as well.

Bodily correspondence: This area is primarily related to the sensory and kinetic organs.

Indications: Scattered lines here indicate a tendency toward neurasthenia, aneurysm, or weakness of the optic nerve.

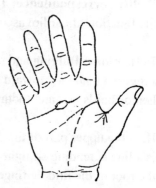

An island-shaped line appearing on the sun mound or on the distal transverse crease indicates poor eyesight. →

4. Water star mound

Location: The mound at the root of the small finger. This is the same location as the mound of Mercury in Western palmistry.

Bodily correspondence: This area is primarily related to the reproductive and respiratory systems.

Indications: Scattered lines here indicate that the function of the reproductive and respiratory organs is incomplete. ➜

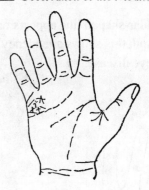

5. First fire star mound

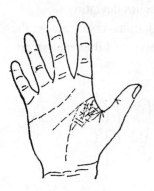

Location: Below the wood phase mound. This location is the same as the so-called active mound of Mars in Western palmistry.

Bodily correspondence: This area is primarily related to the kidneys. Therefore, according to TCM, it reflects the condition of the reproductive and urological systems.

Indications: Scattered lines here show a tendency toward reproductive and urological system diseases. ←

6. Second fire star mound

Location: Below the water phase mound. This location is the same as the so-called passive mound of Mars in Western palmistry.

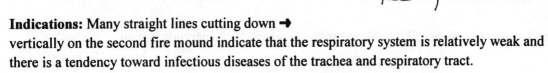

Bodily correspondence: This area is primarily related to the lungs and large intestine.

Indications: Many straight lines cutting down ➜
vertically on the second fire mound indicate that the respiratory system is relatively weak and there is a tendency toward infectious diseases of the trachea and respiratory tract.

If a circular-shaped line appears on the second fire mound, this shows a tendency toward eye disease. ➜

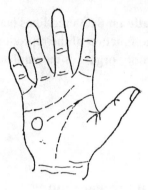

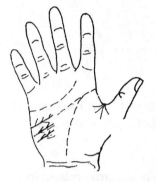

Relatively heavy transverse lines, branches deviating from transverse lines, or several lines cutting transversely across the second fire mound indicate a weak function of the respiratory system.

◆

Well-shaped lines appearing on the second fire mound as well as on the moon mound indicate weak large intestine function. They may also indicate a tendency for infection in either the lungs or large intestine. In the case of the large intestine, this may manifest as diarrhea or colitis. ➜

7. Moon mound

Location: Below the second fire mound. This is the same location as the mound of the Moon in Western palmistry as well.

Bodily correspondence: This area is primarily related to the nervous system.

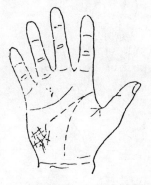

Indications: Scattered lines here indicate pathological changes in kidneys and bladder, kidney stones, diminished visual acuity, gout, and anemia as well as gynecological disease.

A deep, long vertical line running downward and cut by a transverse line indicates a painful *bi* disease in the area of the foot. ➡

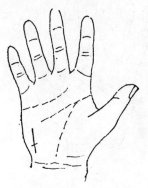

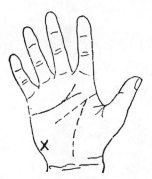

If there is a thick, heavy, cross-shaped line and the heaven or distal transverse crease consists of two lines, side by side below the index finger, this shows a tendency toward gout.
⬅

If the color of the moon mound is black and there is a dark black color on the earth or radial longitudinal crease near the wrist, these indicate dysentery and different types of chronic enteritis.
➡

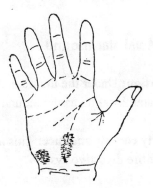

63

Fragmentary black dots here
indicate a weak digestive function.
➡

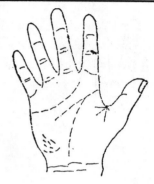

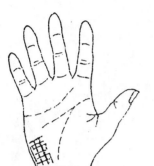

Vertical and transverse lines appearing and forming
scattered squares in the middle of this mound or on the
lower part of the moon mound indicate a tendency
toward kidney infection or diabetes. However, if these
are present on a female, they usually indicate uterine
disease.
⬅

Star-shaped lines appearing on the lower
part of the moon mound indicate a tendency
toward pathological changes in the
urological system. After middle age,
they indicate a tendency toward diabetes.
➡

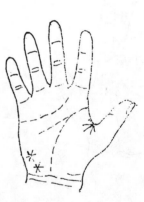

8. Metal star mound

Location: Under the thumb and surrounded by the earth or radial longitudinal crease. This is
the same location as the mound of Venus in Western palmistry.

Bodily correspondence: This mound is primarily related to the spleen and stomach, including
the entire digestive system.

Indications: Hair-shaped lines appearing on the metal phase mound indicate a tendency toward pathological changes of the nerves and vitality. They are usually due to an imbalanced lifestyle. ➜

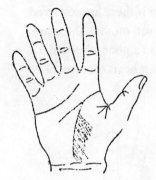

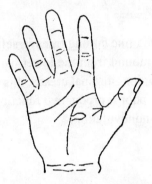

An eye-shaped line appearing on this mound that transversely contacts the earth or radial longitudinal crease indicates a personal tragedy, depression, and lost confidence.

⬅

A cloudy, greenish-black color at the lower part of the metal phase mound indicates poor function of the digestive system. ➜

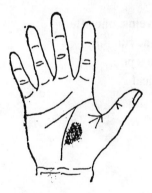

9. Soil mound

Location: The lower or proximal part of the palm. This is the same location as the mound of Neptune in Western palmistry.

Bodily correspondence: This area corresponds to the reproductive and endocrine systems.

Indications: If there are scattered lines on the soil mound, these are usually due to a poor inherited constitution or heart disease. ➤

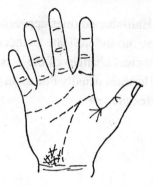

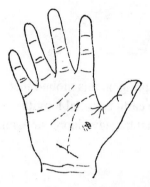

If there is a slanted line cutting transversely down to the soil mound from the lower part of the earth or radial longitudinal crease, this usually indicates poor reproductive function or infertility due to nonovulation. ←

If there are visible blue veins, one after another from the wrist line running upward, this also indicates poor reproductive and urological system function. ➤

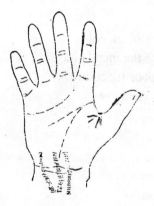

Palm Flexure Lines

When most people think of palmistry, they think of the lines in the palm. Indeed, even in Chinese, palmistry is often called *shou wen xue*, the study of the lines in the hand. Not only are the flexure lines of the palm different from person to person but they also change with the condition of one's health and with age. Thus the lines in the palm can convey volumes of information on a person's health as well as every other aspect of their life.

The palm flexure lines include the three main creases seen on the palm of the hand. These are (1) the earth or radial longitudinal crease (called the life line in Western palmistry), (2) the human or proximal transverse crease (called the head line in Western palmistry), and (3) the heaven or distal transverse creases (called the heart line in Western palmistry). ➜

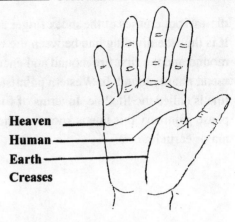

Besides these three major creases, there are a number of other smaller creases. These are called the health, obstruction, indulgence, sex, Venus or ribbon crease, jade column, Saturn, Sun, and inspiration creases. All of these are related to, and are further reflections of, the original three main creases. ➜

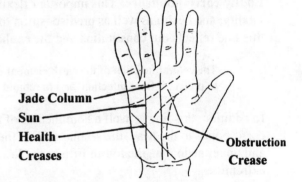

Three Main Creases

In Chinese palmistry, the three main lines in the palm traditionally correspond to the so-called three links (*san gang*) or three powers (*san cai*). These are earth, humanity, and heaven. When one combines these three powers with the five phases and seven planets above, one sees the reflection of the entire Chinese cosmos in the palm of one's hand. The cosmological significance of the palm becomes even more apparent when one learns that the four seasons and the twelve months of the year are also given their corresponding places on the palm in traditional Chinese palmistry. In addition, all the lines in the hand correspond to one or another of the five phases.

1. Earth crease

Location: The earth crease surrounds the whole thenar eminence. In anatomical terms, the earth crease is the radial longitudinal crease. A normal earth crease begins in between the

digital root creases of the index finger and thumb.
It is thus the dividing line between the wood
mound and the first fire mound and encircles the
metal phase mound. In Western palmistry, this
line is called the life line. In terms of five
phase palmistry this line is known as the
major earth line. ➜

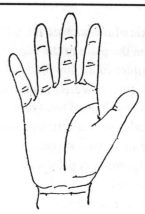

Bodily correspondence: This important flexure line indicates a person's basic physique, vitality, and health as well as predisposition to disease. Just as the body is built from earth, so this line reflects our constitution and the exuberance of our qi. Terence Dukes explains:

> The central function of the earth element is to preserve and balance the body's energies, to protect it from infection, and to rebuild it in case of injury.

In addition, this line is itself a homunculus of the entire body. The first fifth of this line corresponds to the head, the second fifth to the neck and shoulders, the third fifth to the chest and upper abdomen, the fourth fifth to the lower abdomen, and the lower fifth to the lower extremities.

Indications: If this line's starting point location is normal, then the body's yin and yang are balanced and one's emotions are healthy.

If its starting point tends to be too high, this indicates that the gallbladder qi tends to be too strong. In TCM, the gallbladder is the official in charge of decision-making. In addition, the liver will also tend to be effulgent. Nevertheless, the body is basically healthy.

If its starting point tends to be too low, this indicates a lack of both vitality and tenacity.

The earth crease surrounds the metal mound. A well-developed metal mound will set off the earth crease very obviously. In that case, the metal mound is surrounded by the earth crease, which covers a large area forming a large crescent shape. If the middle of this arch extends to the central line made by extending a line down from the center of the middle finger, this indicates good health and full vitality and is a symbol of longevity.

68

If the amplitude of the arch made by the earth crease is shallow and its central portion does not extend as far out into the center of the palm, this indicates a weak physique. In either sex, it also indicates a tendency toward infertility.

This is why the earth crease is often called the body's life line. It should be long, deep, clear, and continuous and the area it surrounds should be large and wide with a red, ruddy complexion free from blemish. All of these are signs of good health. ➜

An earth crease that runs to the moon mound indicates a weak physique with insufficient energy and vitality. It further indicates the possibility of gynecological disease such as infertility.

As mentioned above, a thick, large, deep earth crease indicates a strong, healthy body. If this appears on both hands, it is an even stronger sign of sufficient energy and vitality.

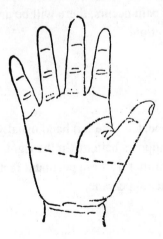

If the palm prints are orderly and uncomplicated and this crease's termination gets thinner and thinner until it gradually disappears, this indicates the ideal of a healthy body. However, if the same thick, large, and deep earth crease suddenly breaks and disappears, it shows a tendency toward apoplexy, including cerebral hemorrhage. ⬅

An earth crease that appears slender compared to the other two main creases is a sign of poor health and body weakness. It also shows a low resistance to disease with insufficient energy and vitality.

If the earth crease has a chain-like appearance, this indicates a weak constitution. It shows the possibility of chronic diseases of the gastrointestinal system. If the upper part of the crease appears like a chain, it indicates that an unhealthy condition occurred during childhood and youth. If the lower part of the line appears like a chain, this indicates an unhealthy condition occurring during adulthood and old age. →

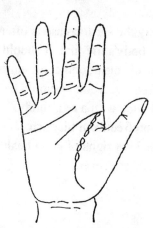

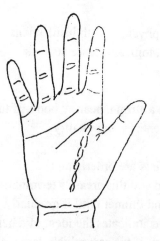

An earth crease appearing like a rope indicates insufficient physical strength and a tendency to be nervous. When facing a crowd or any extraordinary situation, individuals with this sign tend to be nervous and shy and may even become speechless. At other times, if even a small pain occurs, there will be an abnormal nervous reaction.
←

When one observes the earth crease, both hands need to be inspected. The left hand usually represents hereditary information. Thus, if the left palm print appears better than the right, this can be related to postnatal lifestyle, environment, profession, or diet. If these postnatal factors are conquered, the right hand earth crease will change to a better appearance.

If the earth crease has a break on its line, no matter what its shape, this is a dangerous sign. If such a break occurs on only one palm, the condition will be comparably light. If it shows up on both palms, this indicates a tendency to easily become ill. ➜

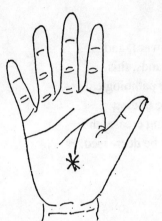

A star-shaped line within such a breaking point is a sign of sudden illness. ➜

If the earth crease becomes wider, this is often seen in chronic dysentery or malnutrition. If a broken section of the earth crease is blocked or cut by a horizontal line, this indicates that an acute disease will occur. It is even more meaningful if this appears on both hands. ⬅

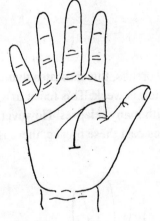

If the broken part of the earth crease is continued by another crease due to a partial overlapping of the original line, this indicates that any pathological change that occurs will be minor. ➜

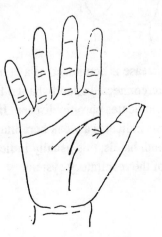

71

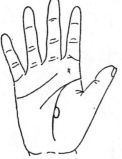

An island-shaped appearance on the earth crease usually indicates hemorrhoids and various types of occult bleeding. It may also be caused by pathological changes due to surgery or trauma. In this latter case, the fact that the line has broken and then came back together shows that the disease is recoverable or self-limiting. ←

If the earth crease suddenly hooks inward, and especially so if this occurs on both hands, this indicates the possibility that an acute pathological change will occur. However, if, at the ending point of this hook, there is a continuing crease, the likelihood of disease occurrence will be decreased. →

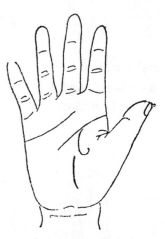

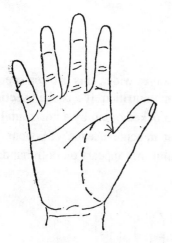

If the earth crease has tiny breaks, this indicates that one's entire physical function is weak. This tends to suggest chronic disease with many relapses. However, as long as the line continues past these breaks, there is the possibility of recovery.
←

If the earth crease is composed of a continuous series of interconnected island-shaped lines, this usually indicates chronic disease. If seen only on the left hand, this indicates a weak hereditary physique. If seen on both hands, this usually indicates a chronic pathology of the respiratory system. →

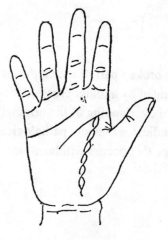

Island-shaped lines also have a close relationship with cancer. If the position of the island-shaped line is close to the top of the starting point of the earth crease, this is usually a sign of nasopharyngeal carcinoma and laryngeal cancer. If it is within the mid-section of this crease, it usually relates to lung, breast, or stomach cancer. If it is seen at the end point of this crease in males, it usually indicates prostate cancer, while in females, it usually relates to uterine cancer. However, the reliability of these observations still needs further research.

A tassel-like line occurring at the ending point of the earth crease indicates an emotional nature, depressed qi, and excessive worry. It also indicates weak physical function and insufficient qi. It is easy for such individuals to become fatigued.
←

In over 300 cases of female infertility, it has been observed that an abnormally high percentage of these women had a hair-shaped or tree root-shaped line at the ending point of their earth crease. Additional signs were a short small finger with an especially short, small, middle phalanx and a deviated fingertip as well as a shallow, light sex crease. Other signs of infertility in these women's palms were water phase mounds that tended to be recessed with scattered lines and soil mounds that tended to be recessed and had no flesh but did have a blue vein on them. In addition, discontinuous, scattered wrist creases as well as the ending point of the earth crease being cut off by a deep, heavy, horizontal crease also tend to indicate female infertility.

A hair-shaped line occurring on one single side at the lower part of the earth crease indicates that the body is weak with the tendency for fatigue. →

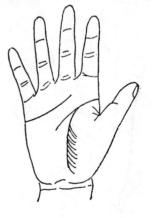

An island-shaped line at the end point
of the earth crease indicates that,
in old age, there will
be chronic disease. ➔

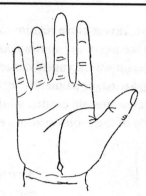

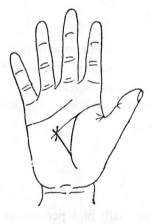

If another line forks off at the low part of the earth
crease and extends to the proximal transverse crease
forming a star-shaped line at that point, this indicates
weak reproductive function. If this is seen during
pregnancy, the position of fetus and the blood pressure
of the mother both need to be checked often in order to
avoid miscarriage.
◀

If the starting point of a female's earth crease
is normal but then, from the middle of the crease,
it suddenly veers toward the moon mound, this
indicates gynecological disease. ➔

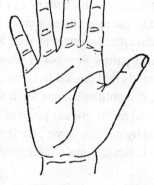

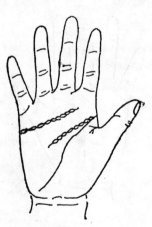

If the ending point of the earth crease veers
toward the moon mound and both the heaven
crease and the proximal transverse crease have
chain-shaped lines, this usually indicates
insufficient physical strength.
◀

If an infant has a chain-shaped line on its
earth crease and a star-shaped line appears
on this chain-shaped line, this indicates
that the child suffers from congenital
insufficiency. Such an infant will be difficult
to raise and will have a tendency toward
dermatological diseases. ➜

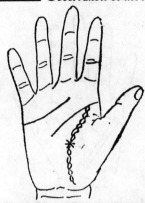

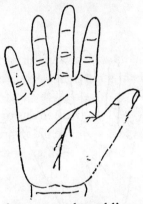

An obvious cross-shaped line and a star-shaped
line appearing on the inner or outer sides
of the earth crease indicate a
condition of poor health. ➜

If there are several branches forking
downward off from the middle of the earth
crease, this indicates a pathological change is
going to happen.
⬅

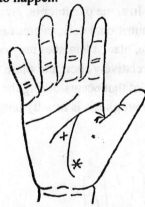

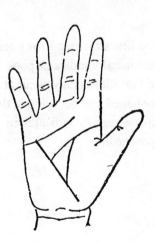

If the health crease connects with the earth
crease, this indicates a tendency toward heart
and cerebrovascular disease. This sign is more
meaningful after middle age.
⬅

75

If two parallel health creases connect with the earth crease and then go upward toward the small finger, this indicates a disorganized, chaotic lifestyle, addiction to drugs, alcohol, and/or cigarettes, or overindulgence in sex which has damaged the health.

Many small blemishes appearing on the earth crease with a decrease in physical strength and vitality are an indication of a pathology about to occur. Obvious blemishes with a red color indicate febrile disease. In acute pneumonia, green blemishes may occur. In nutritional deficiencies caused by a parasitic disease, black blemishes may occur. If the earth crease is relatively short and there is a blemish at its ending point that occurs during the disease period, then the prognosis is usually unfavorable. →

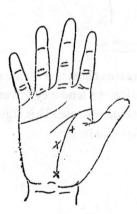

A cross-shaped line attaching to any section of the earth crease usually indicates poor immunity and that illness may occur at any time. A cross-shaped line occuring at the end of the earth crease usually indicates an unfavorable prognosis.

A star-shaped line on both the earth and heaven creases indicates a tendency toward diseases of the lungs and trachea. If there is also a chain-shaped line on the heaven crease, this means that the disease is relatively serious. If the heaven crease is complete and straight, however, then the disease will be relatively light. ➜

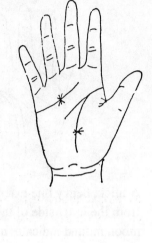

If the ending point of the earth crease is surrounded by scattered, triangular-shaped lines, this indicates an increased chance of angiocardiopathy in one's old age. ➜

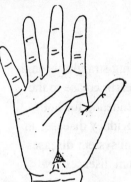

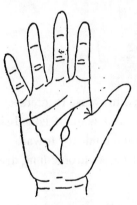

An island-shaped line on the earth crease and a health crease looking like a crawling snake indicate abnormal bile secretion and poor gallbladder function. People who have these shaped lines in their palms should pay attention to their diet. They should eat foods that are easily digested and they should avoid fatty, oily, and heavy-tasting food, such as red meat, spicy foods, alcohol, and so on.
⬅

If there is an island-shaped line on the earth crease and the complexion on the moon mound is greenish and dull, this indicates relatively weak kidney function with a tendency toward urological and reproductive system diseases. ➜

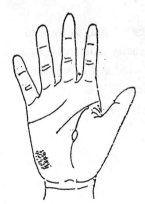

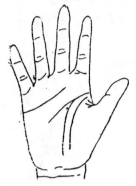

If there is an assisting line running parallel along the inner side of the earth crease, this indicates that the righteous qi is sufficient and the person has a strong physical ability. In Western palmistry, this is referred to as a double life line. ←

A thick, heavy line extending straight through from the inner side of the earth crease to the moon mound indicates a tendency for both kidney and lung diseases. Kidney diseases in TCM include both urological system diseases and also reproductive system diseases. →

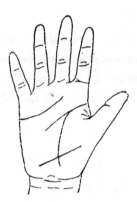

If the starting part of the earth crease is intersected by some longitudinal lines as well as many island-shaped lines, these usually indicate a tendency toward pulmonary tuberculosis or other chronic lung disease. ←

A comparatively large opening at the end of the earth crease usually indicates *feng shi*. Literally this means wind and dampness but functionally it means rheumatic complaints. →

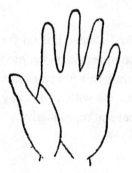

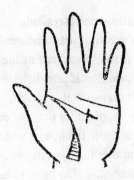

Triangular-shaped lines at the end of the earth crease or a cross-shaped line in the middle of the palm usually indicate heart disease.

An earth crease that does not arc but rather drops down in a straight line or appears like a wave may indicate diabetes. →

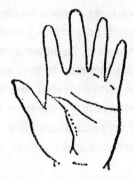

If the earth crease looks like a wave, it may also indicate weakness of the cardiovascular system. In that case, there is the possibility of a myocardial infarction and/or arteriosclerosis.

If the earth crease is light and shallow and the three main creases have small brown lumps that do not change color even when pressed, these are signs often seen in cerebral hemorrhage. →

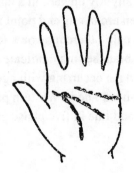

In addition, an earth crease with a bluish-green or whitish color indicates weak physical strength, anemia, or depressed, *i.e.*, static, blood. If the earth crease is green, it may further indicate abnormal digestion, assimilation, and nutritional absorption. If the lower half of the earth crease is dark black, this indicates parasitic disease. An earth crease that is purplish indicates a virus that has invaded the blood, or syphilis, while an earth crease that is a rich, dark, reddish-purple is an indication of effulgent liver fire. The reader should note that the earth crease can be read in terms of several variables. On the one hand, it can note the age at which a pathology may occur depending on where an abnormal sign appears on this line, youth being read at the top of this line and old age being read at its bottom. This line may also be read as the spinal column with diseases of the upper spinal column being read at the upper part of the line, and so on. Further, this line may be read as the digestive tract, with the upper line corresponding to the upper part of the digestive tract. And finally, this line may simply be read as an indicator of health and vitality. Thus what this line indicates depends on the patient's history and condition, and the practitioner must remain flexible to its interpretation depending on the circumstances in each case and on other signs and symptoms

2. Human crease

Location: A normal human crease is located in the center of the palm, starting from the area below the wood mound and above the first fire mound. From there it typically slants transversely downward. However, the depth of this downward curve is variable as is the length of this line. In anatomical terms, this is the proximal transverse crease. This crease should be thick, deep, long, clear, and continuous. Its color should be healthy and fresh. In shape, it should extend slightly upward in a curve, thus describing an arc. At its end point near the center of the palm, there may be a few branches. These branches may indicate different pathological changes occurring with age. This line is called the head line in Western palmistry and the major wood line in five phase palmistry. ➜

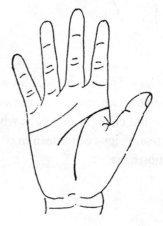

Bodily correspondences: This line has a close relationship with the cerebrum and nervous system function. For this reason it is called in Western palmistry the head line. In Chinese palmistry, it is referred to as the human crease and also as the brain crease. Therefore, this line particularly indicates the vitality and health of the nervous system. It also corresponds with the eyes, ears, nose, and throat as well as with IQ.

Indications: A normal human crease usually indicates good health, full vitality, and cheerfulness. Among intellectuals, the end point often curves down deeply, while if it is flat and straight, this shows a narrower, more material frame of mind.

If the human crease curves down all the way to the moon mound, this generally indicates weak physiological function and often shows insufficient central qi. ➡

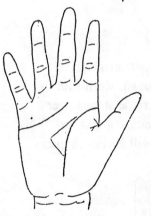

An excessively short human crease indicates insufficient qi, laziness, and lack of ambition.

An excessively shallow and faint human crease running close to the earth crease indicates insufficient qi with a tendency toward headaches and dizziness. ➡

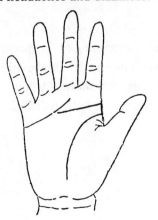

When the human crease is flat and straight, keeping its distance from the earth crease, the individual is overly frank and lacks humor.
⬅

A thin human crease extending down to the moon or soil mounds, which runs together with the earth crease for an excessive length indicates a weak vitality and weak nervous system. The individual is often over-sensitive and tends to be either phonophobic or photophobic. ➜

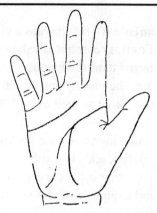

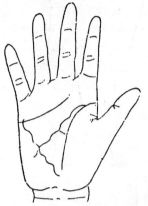

If the human crease and the health crease both have wavy lines, this indicates a tendency for cerebral disease. It also shows weak vitality, lack of patience, and tendency toward vacillation. ←

When a branch from the human crease meets the heaven crease and the health crease joins the earth crease at the lower part of the palm, this indicates that, in old age, hypertension will lead to apoplexy. ➜

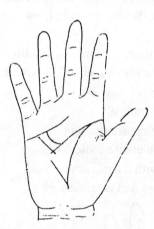

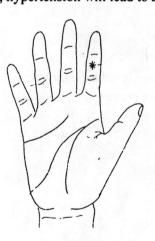

If there is a human crease extending to the moon mound and a star-shaped line appears on the middle phalanx of the index finger, this shows a tendency toward mental illness or nervous system disorders. ←

A human crease having an obvious wave-shaped line indicates the possibility of acquiring a nervous system disorder.
➡

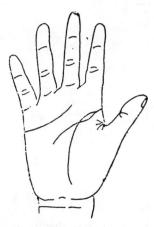

If the human crease has various widths or is too thick and is bisected, this usually indicates cerebral hemorrhage. A faint human crease indicates the strong possibility of cerebral or nervous disease. And an absent or hard to see human crease indicates undeveloped intelligence or feeble-mindedness.
⬅

If an obvious island-shaped line appears at the puncture of the human and earth creases, this indicates poor nutrition in one's youth.
⬅

An island-shaped line appearing on the human crease below the middle finger that does not reach the jade column crease usually indicates neurasthenia caused by mental and physical exhaustion. ➡

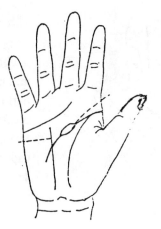

An island-shaped line on the human crease below the ring finger indicates excessive mental activity and a relatively weak optic nerve with excessive eye fatigue. In advanced age, there is a tendency toward cataracts. ←

If the human crease ends below the ring finger with a large island-shaped line occurring there, this indicates a pathological change of the nerves of the cerebrum. An earth crease also connecting with the health crease is a sign of a cerebrovascular pathology. →

A thin human crease extending down to the area of the soil or moon mounds with an island-shaped line at the end indicates an unsociable disposition and nervousness. →

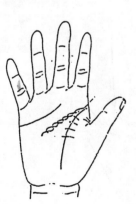

A chain-like human crease indicates nervous problems and lack of tenacity and inconsistency. If the starting part of the earth crease is also cut by a number of obstructing transverse lines, this indicates weak respiratory system function and insufficient vital capacity. ←

A human crease having obvious cross-shaped lines, even if very small, indicates an unstable psychological condition. They further indicate insufficiency of the righteous qi, weak gallbladder qi, and fearfulness. ➡

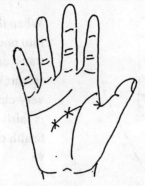

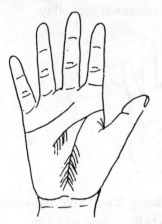

Tassel-like lines appearing on both human and earth creases indicate weak physical ability, insufficient tenacity, and fatigue.
⬅

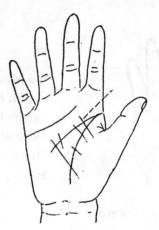

Scattered lines in the middle of the palm with many obstruction creases crossing both the earth and human creases indicate nervousness. In a child, these indicate bed wetting at night. ➡

A short, light human crease indicates a weak digestive system.

A human crease whose starting part extends to the edge of the palm is termed a Sydney line. This is so named because it was notice in Sydney, Australia, around the 1970s. It is related to leukemia and other types of cancers. ➡

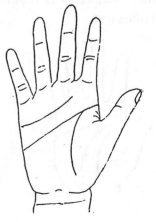

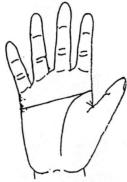

When the human and heaven creases are conjoined into one, this is usually called a Simian crease, a transverse palm, or an unobstructed palm. Some researchers consider it a sign of congenital aplasia. A very clear and complete crease indicates that the health is fairly good. A discontinuous crease shows a weak health condition and emotional instability. ←

If, at the terminal sections of the human, earth, and heaven creases, there are cutting lines, these may indicate lung disease. →

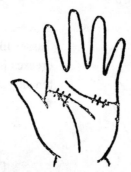

If a human crease extends down to the hypothenar area, if there are cuts in the crease with many longitudinal lines, and if, at the same time, there many longitudinal lines appearing at the root of the small finger, this suggests a tendency toward cystitis. ←

A human crease curving toward the thumb indicates the possibility of mental illness. →

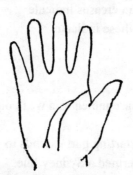

A human crease having many small island-shaped lines indicates cerebral illness. ←

86

Different colors appearing on the
human crease have different meanings.
If the human crease has black dots
or stains, this indicates the
possibility of a cerebral tumor. ➡

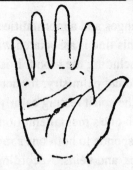

A dry, hot, red color indicates a tendency toward hypertension with the possibility of encephalemia due to an effulgent liver. The appearance of a greenish-white color indicates qi vacuity and a weak physique. In this case there is both insufficient qi and blood and the tendency for cerebral anemia.

A pale color with black dots on a human crease that has a forking line traveling upward near the starting point of the earth crease indicates the tendency for pathological changes of the cerebral vasculature. Headaches may be a common symptom. The human crease usually predicts hereditary conditions.

3. Heaven crease

Location: A healthy heaven crease starts from the ulnar side of the palm in the area below the water phase mound, which is in turn below the little finger. It then runs transversely across the palm underneath the sun and earth phase mounds.
The heaven crease may run relatively horizontally
across the palm or curve upward to end between
the earth and wood mounds. In anatomical terms,
this is the distal transverse crease. It should be long,
deep, and clear with a fresh, healthy color. There should
be a few branches extending downward with more
branches and assistant creases extending upward.
This line is called the heart line in Western palmistry.
In five phase palmistry, this line is called the major
water line. ➡

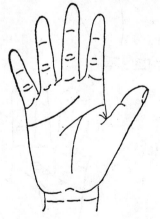

Bodily correspondences: Changes and abnormalities in this line reflect both mental and physical conditions. Because this line is associated with the water phase, it corresponds with all of the yin fluids in the body, including the blood. It is this relationship to blood that links this line to the heart in Chinese medical palmistry, for according to TCM, it is blood which nourishes the heart and keeps the spirit resting calmly within the heart. Thus the heart in Chinese medicine includes both one's mental/emotional activities as well as cardiovascular function, and so this line corresponds to both one's mental/emotional well-being as well as to the health of their heart, arteries, and veins. According to Terence Duke and from the perspective of Western medicine, this line may be seen as reflecting the supportive, parasympathetic actions of the physical organs and nervous system.

Indications: A normal heaven crease reflects a personality full of emotions, loving life, with good, complete heart function.

If the heaven crease breaks into tiny sections, having scattered lines, chain-shaped lines, or is a wave-shaped line, all of these indicate the tendency for heart and cerebrovascular disease. Individuals with this type of crease tend to be indecisive or inconsistent.

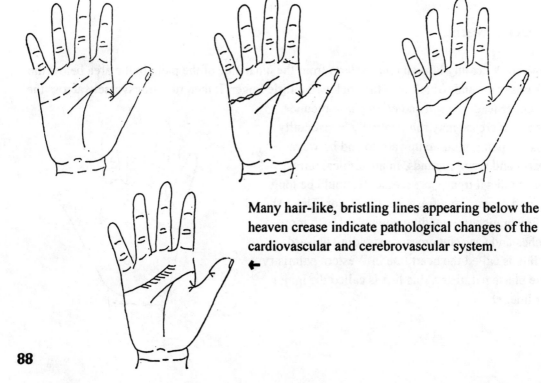

Many hair-like, bristling lines appearing below the heaven crease indicate pathological changes of the cardiovascular and cerebrovascular system.

When, under the small or ring finger, the heaven crease does not continue toward the edge of the palm but instead hooks back upward, this indicates a tendency toward heart disease. ➜

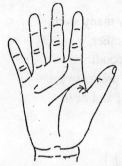

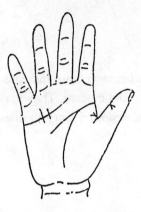

If the heaven crease is cut straight by two short, straight, heavy lines under the ring finger, this usually indicates hypertension.
◄

If the heaven crease has a large break under the area between the middle and ring fingers, this indicates a circulatory or respiratory system problem. ➜

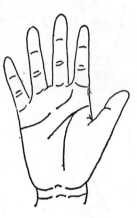

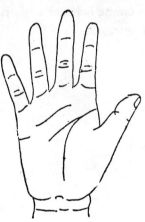

If the heaven crease has a large break under the small finger, this indicates the tendency for a liver problem.
◄

If the heaven crease is cut by many short,
straight creases, one after another,
this indicates a weak health condition.
In this case, one should take preventive
health care measures, or liver and heart
disease may manifest. ➜

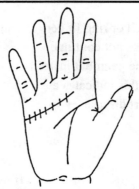

Island-shaped lines on the heaven crease indicate
pathological changes in the optic nerve. They may also
indicate a tendency toward venous aneurysm disease
in the vascular system.
◄

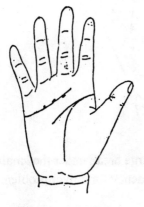

Black dots on the heaven crease indicate a relatively
weak heart and irregular heartbeat.
◄

If the three main creases start from the
same point and the human crease is short
with a star-shaped line at its end point,
these are usually the signs of a suddenly
occurring, serious pathology. ➜

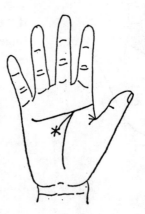

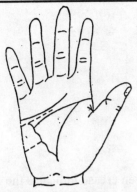

The space between the heaven crease and the human crease is called in Chinese palmistry the square front courtyard. A narrow "square front courtyard" (fang-ting) and a wave-shaped health crease indicate insufficient righteous qi and a tendency toward infectious diseases. ⬅

Two strip-like lines at the ulnar side of the heaven crease usually indicate gout. ➡

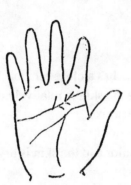

If the beginning part of the heaven crease is cut into a rib-like shape, this usually indicates pulmonary tuberculosis. ➡

If there is a light heaven crease that looks like twisting waves with cutting lines (#1 below) or a few slanted lines mingling between the heaven and human creases (#2 below), this may indicate heart disease.

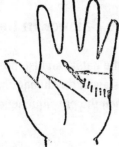

#1   #2

Longitudinal lines on the heaven crease indicate a tendency toward laryngopharyngitis and carcinoma of the larynx. ➜

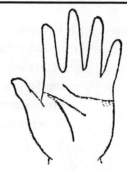

An excessively long heaven crease indicates the tendency for nervous gastrointestinal problems.

Small island-shaped lines appearing on the heaven crease usually indicate neurasthenia.

The color of the heaven crease also has a close relationship with the circulation of the heart. If the heaven crease appears red and the skin is relatively dry, this indicates a tendency toward hypertension or cerebrovascular disease.

If the heaven crease is a grayish color and the skin is dry, this indicates pathological changes in the liver.

Long-term smoking or alcohol and/or drug use can harm the central nervous and heart circulatory systems. In that case, the heaven crease will be dark colored or a coin-sized darkish area will appear. The heaven crease may have numerous tiny breaks.

The Three Main Creases and Acid & Alkaline Balance in the Body

The distribution and distance of the three main creases on the palm can also be used to determine the acid and alkaline balance of the body. For instance, the thenar eminence mound corresponds to the body's acidity. If this is large and full, then the physique tends to be acidic.

One can also use the heaven crease as the upper border and the human crease as the lower border. Then use the line extended from between the base of the small and ring fingers proximal toward the wrist as the left border and the line extended from between the base of the index and middle finger proximal toward the wrist as the right border. The *Ming Tang* area is thus within these four borders. This area corresponds to the body's alkalinity. The larger the area of the *Ming Tang* is, the more alkaline the body, whereas, if the *Ming Tang* is very narrow, the body tends to be acidic.

If the human crease is long transversely, this represents another sign that the body tends to be acidic. But, if the human crease curves down excessively, this indicates that the body tends to be alkaline.

In terms of tendency toward disease, different acid and alkaline bodies tend to suffer from different types of illnesses. Acidic physiques tend to suffer from hypertension, arteriosclerosis, cerebral hemorrhage, and diabetes, whereas, alkaline physiques tend to suffer from low blood pressure, asthma, gastroptosis, or cancer.

Minor Creases

Besides the three main creases, related smaller creases are also important in determining health and disease. These smaller creases, known as the minor lines, are associated with and reflective of the major lines. Therefore, they are sometimes called reflections of the major lines and tend to show these major lines' subtler activities. However, not every individual has every one of the following smaller creases. According to Terence Dukes:

> When minor lines are very pronounced, we know that an organic function has been made conscious; it or its paradigm has been brought to the surface for some reason. This is not natural; it is like snow in July. We find that most minor lines appear only when major lines are functioning at less than optimum energy.

93

This is why some palmists say that it is better not to have most of these minor lines. On the other hand, if one does have any of these minor lines, it is generally better that they be unbroken, unobstructed, and unblemished.

1. Health crease

Location: This crease starts from below the water mound where it may cross the heaven crease and slants diagonally downward toward the thenar eminence or metal mound. (As a rule, it does not connect with the earth crease.) In five phase palmistry, this line is called a minor wood line. ➡

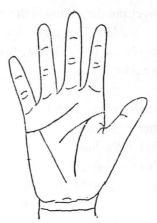

Bodily correspondences: The health crease does not correspond to a body part or specific organs. Rather it indicates the severity and progression of disease. Terence Dukes further clarifies this by saying that the presence of a health crease is a sign that the bodily metabolism is hyperactive and that it typically only appears as a sign of imbalance.

Indications: Its best not to have a health crease. However, if one has a health crease, it will tend to get deeper during the course of any disease that gets worse or as the health deteriorates. Conversely, as the health improves, the health crease also tends to become shallower and lighter. Very short creases or health creases that change color are warning signs of severe problems.

A health crease that touches the earth crease usually indicates angiocardiopathy. ➡

The health crease should not cross the earth crease. If it does, it usually indicates weakness of the viscera and bowels and especially the heart.

If there are blemishes on the health crease, acute disease may appear suddenly at any time. ➜

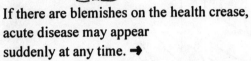

An island-shaped line at the end of the health crease or scattered lines around such an island-shaped line indicate respiratory disease.

Many island-shaped lines forming a chain-shaped line on the health crease also indicate respiratory system problems, while a health crease made up of many striations also suggests respiratory problems primarily due to stress. A striated health crease also suggests that the person is very sensitive and, therefore, overreactive to stimuli. ➜

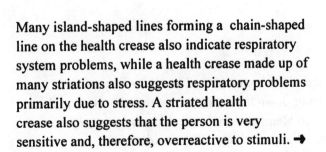

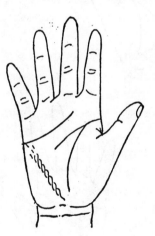

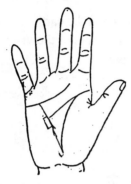

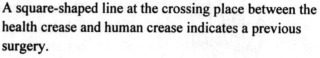

A square-shaped line at the crossing place between the health crease and human crease indicates a previous surgery.

If the health crease looks like a crawling snake and the human crease appears weak and broken, this indicates digestive system disease.

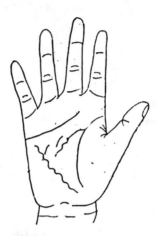

If the middle phalanges of the index and ring fingers appear long and the health crease looks like a crawling snake, this indicates incomplete calcium assimilation. Skeletal and dental decay may thus appear early.

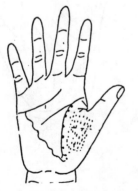

If the health crease looks like a crawling snake, extends down to connect to the earth crease, and there are red blemishes on the earth crease, such signs usually appear along with heart disease.

A health crease appearing weak with tiny breaks indicates a weak digestive system and that the physical strength is affected. If the health crease appears weak and the distance between the heaven crease and human crease is narrow, these signs indicate that the trachea and brachus may easily become infected, often followed by asthma. ➜

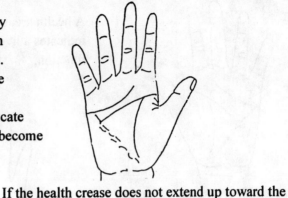

If the health crease does not extend up toward the small finger but instead looks like many scattered lines at the edge of the palm, this indicates impaired physical strength due to irregular lifestyle. This, in turn, causes insufficient energy. ⬅

A short, deep health crease cutting through both the heaven and human creases indicates cerebral disease. ➜

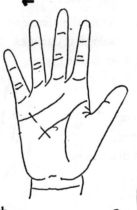

If the health crease appears weak with tiny breaks, all three main creases appear shallow and weak, and on the lower part of the earth crease there are feather-shaped lines extending downward, these all indicate a very insufficient physical condition and chronic consumptive disease. ➜

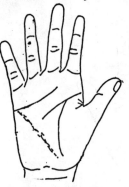

A health crease that appears now and again usually indicates a liver problem or weak digestive system function.
←

A short health crease appearing in the middle of the palm usually indicates heart disease.
→

If the color of the crease and the area around the crease appear light gray, dark red, brown, or red, this indicates the possibility of pathological changes in the digestive system. The normal color of the crease should be a light, pinkish-red.

If the area where the health and heaven creases meet has a dark red appearance, this indicates the possibility of heart disease. →

A health crease having dark brown spots indicates a severe problem and especially the possibility of cancer.
←

Although the health crease can indicate recent health conditions, other creases also need to be taken into account in order to make a precise judgment about the person's state of health.

2. Jade column crease

Location: This crease starts from the lower part of the palm, crosses the center of the palm, and extends straight to the root of the middle finger. It is also called the career crease and in Western palmistry is called the fate line. In Chinese five phase palmistry, this line is called the minor earth line. This line always ends on or is oriented toward the earth mound below the middle finger. Any line that does not terminate in this direction is not, in fact, a jade column line but some other minor line. →

In contradistinction to the three main creases, a normal jade column crease should not be too thick. The best one is thin, shallow, straight upward, clear, and constant. The color should be a light, pinkish-red. Unlike the health crease, which is better not to have, this is one minor line that one should have.

Bodily correspondence: The jade column crease delineates a person's social relationships. Just as the major earth line delineates one's grounding in their physical body, the jade column crease represents our balance within the world at large and our ability to live life with measure and self-control. According to Terence Dukes, as long as this line is present, our relationships with the outside world and our own inner nature remain balanced and communicate with each other. Because this is an earth line, this line does also have a relationship to one's physical structure, digestive system, and nutritional balance.

Indications: When the jade column crease looks like a wave, it indicates an unsatisfied mental state and possible pathological changes due to emotional shock and emotional exhaustion. →

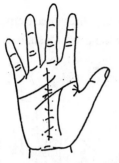

If the jade column crease is cut here and there by short transverse lines, this indicates that the individual has a nervous tendency and a quick temper. It further suggests poor physical strength and chronic disease. ←

A jade column crease starting from the moon mound, extending on a slant toward the index finger, and then ending at the heaven crease is usually due to an irregular lifestyle that has damaged the body. →

If the jade column crease has two continuous island-shaped lines appearing similar to a figure 8, this indicates a tendency toward psychataxia and somnambulism. ←

If the jade column and earth creases both display the same kind of off-and-on breaks, this indicates chronic disease with a long recovery. →

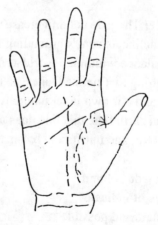

100

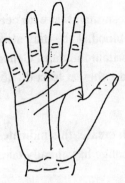

A cross-shaped line at the end point of the jade column crease shows the tendency for apoplexy in the aged, including cerebrovascular accident.

←

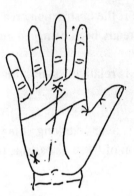

A star-shaped line at the end point of the jade column crease on both hands accompanied by a star-shaped line on the moon mound indicates that the individual lacks endurance, has unstable emotions, and tends to be depressed. →

An island-shaped line on the lower part of the jade column crease indicates a tendency toward neurasthenia.

←

In addition, if the center of the palm across which the jade column runs is a healthy reddish color and is smooth, this indicates health. However, if it appears dark green or pale and dry with scattered lines, then a tendency for sudden disease is indicated.

3. Obstruction creases

Location: This refers to any abnormal crease that transversely cuts any of the main or minor creases. Therefore, such creases' location and shape are not fixed.

Bodily correspondence: Obstruction lines, as their name suggest, manifest with certain types of obstruction, especially of the viscera and bowels and qi and blood. They may also appear in cases of kidney yang weakness, including decrease in adrenocortical function. Generally, obstruction creases do not appear on healthy hands, or, if they do, they at least do not cross over the earth crease.

Indications: If the obstruction crease has crossed over the earth crease, this indicates that the health has already been damaged and that some pathological change has already taken place.

If this crease is relatively short, this indicates that some illness has become a psychological burden.

If the crease is over 1cm long, it may indicate a variety of different types of illness. Differentiation of these diseases is based on the location of the ends of such a crease. For instance:

If an obstruction crease cuts through the earth crease and is located below the ring finger or extends and meets the digital transverse crease, this indicates heart disease. If there is an island-shaped line or a blemish at its ending point, the above meaning is clear and definite. ➜

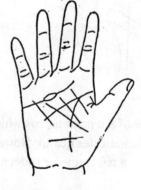

If there are checkered-shaped lines or cross-shaped lines on the lower part of the moon mound and they face an obstruction crease that cuts through the earth crease, these indicate kidney or gynecological disease.
←

If the square front courtyard (*Pang Ting*) is narrow and small and an obstruction crease ends here, this indicates pathological changes in the pulmonary airways. ➜

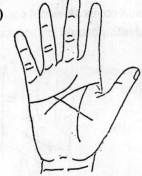

An obstruction crease appearing like an arch and crossing transversely between the human and earth creases is usually due to an uncontrolled diet, which causes stomach and intestinal disease. Such disease may become chronic and cause obstruction of digestion and assimilation. ⬅

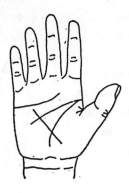

An obstruction crease appearing deep at the human crease and extending to the earth crease indicates even more serious stomach and intestinal disease. ➜

4. Sun crease

Location: This crease is a kind of minor or secondary jade column crease. It is located under the ring finger and is shorter than the jade column crease. Not every individual has this crease. In Western palmistry, it is also called an Apollo or success line. In five phase palmistry, this is a minor fire line and is associated with the jade column crease from which it should derive its support.

Bodily correspondence: The sun crease does not correspond to any particular organ or system. Rather it shows that the individual's persona is acceptable to society. Often this line is simply missing.

Indications: An island-shape line appearing on the sun crease indicates eye disease and especially if an island-shaped line also appears on the earth crease.

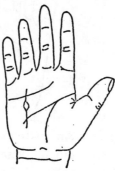

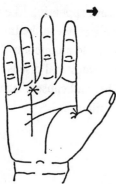

A star-shaped line at the top of the sun crease (especially on both hands) usually indicates nervousness and a tendency toward cerebrovascular disease. ←

If the sun crease curves similar to a wave, this is a sign of exterior repletion and interior vacuity. The seven emotions may also be depressed, and there is a tendency toward neurasthenia and insomnia. →

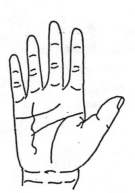

5. Indulgence crease

Location: Indulgence creases are located on the low part of the moon mound. This crease may be thick and long. It may also connect with or cross the earth crease. Not every person has these. In Western palmistry, they are called the *via lasciva* or path of lasciviousness. In five phase palmistry, they are called the lower minor water line.

Bodily correspondence: This crease does not correspond to any particular organ or system. Rather it shows a physical or metabolic sensitivity toward stimulants such as alcohol or drugs.

Indications: This crease typically appears on individuals who have an irregular lifestyle. These individuals stay up late at night and are mentally and physically exhausted. They may use their physical strength excessively or do not control their sexual desire. There may be chronic addictions to cigarettes, alcohol, and/or drugs. The stronger and more pronounced an indulgence line is, the more reactive the individual is. Persons with this line may also suffer from various allergic reactions, such as to anesthetics and common medicines. ➡

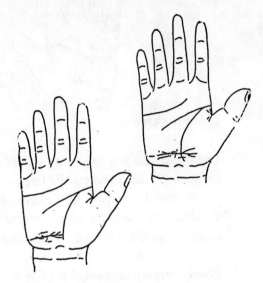

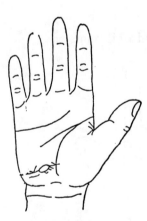

An island-shaped line on the indulgence crease indicates that the overuse of cigarettes or alcohol has caused severe damage to the body and that the person therefore experiences listlessness.
⬅

A checkered-shaped line on the indulgence crease also indicates addiction and damage to the body by smoking, drinking, and overuse of drugs. ➡

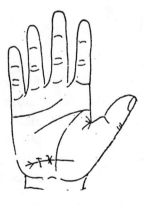

A star-shaped line on the indulgence crease indicates that chronic smoking and the use of alcohol and drugs have caused a toxic invasion and damaged the nervous system.
←

6. Venus crease

Location: This is a downward arched crease that starts from the lower edge of the finger seam between the index and middle fingers. It then curves over to the finger seam between the middle and ring fingers. In Western palmistry, it is called the girdle of Venus. It is above and a subsidiary crease to the heaven crease. Therefore, in five phase palmistry, it is called the higher minor water line. Not every individual has a Venus crease.

Bodily correspondence: This line is related to kidney yang and all its functions.

Indications: When the Venus crease is complete, beautifully arched, and has hardly any breaks, this indicates that the function of the brain and the central nerve system are complete and healthy. →

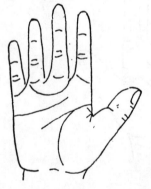

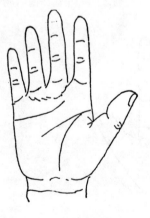

Tiny breaks in the Venus crease indicate that the function of the urological system is relatively weak. It further indicates allergies and is also seen in drug or alcohol toxicity. Tiny breaks on the Venus crease may also indicate low progesterone level affecting the luteal phase and pregnancy. The result may be infertility. ←

A blemish on the Venus crease
shows a tendency toward
urological system disease. ➡

7. The Circle of Saturn

Location: The circle of Saturn is located at the bottom of the root of the middle finger and looks like an arched, crescent-shaped semi-circle. Not everyone has this line.

Bodily correspondence: This line does not correspond to any particular organ or system. Like other of the minor lines, it corresponds more to psychological traits whose expression may have an impact on a person's health and well being.

Indications: This line usually occurs on people who are unsocial, narrow-minded, and very jealous. ➡

8. Inspiration crease

Location: This line starts from the moon mound and extends to the small finger. Not everyone has such a line.

Bodily correspondence: This line is also called the sleepwalking crease. Rather than being related to a particular organ or system, it is related to this specific pathology.

Indications: An island-shaped line in the inspiration crease indicates somnambulism or sleepwalking. ➡

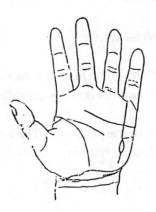

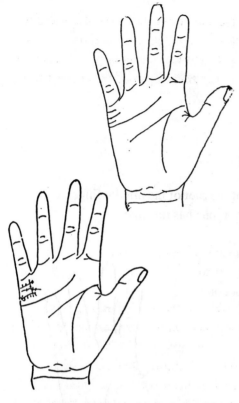

9. Sex crease

Location: These are short transverse creases that are located above the heaven crease and below the root of the small finger. In China, most individuals have two or three sex creases. The best ones should be deep, smooth, straight, clear, and tidy. The color should be a healthy pinkish-red. ◄

Bodily correspondence: Such lines indicate sufficient kidney qi and normal sex function. In Western palmistry, they are called marriage lines.

Indications: If the sex creases are scattered, have forked branches, or the small finger is short, small, and crooked, this usually indicates impotence or infertility. ◄

Sex creases that are short, shallow, faint, and hard to see with a light color are usually due to decreased sexual function or infertility. On a female, this indicates lack of sex drive or even a dislike of sex.

10. Wrist crease

Location: These lines or creases are located just below the center of the lower part of the palm where the wrist is. They are called the bracelets in Western palmistry.

Bodily correspondence: The wrist crease helps to judge the condition of the urological and reproductive systems.

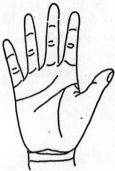

Indications: If there are more than two wrist creases and these creases are very clear and continuous, they indicate good health and vigorous vitality. This is even more meaningful when accompanied by a thick earth mound. ⬅

An incomplete wrist crease that is broken or obvious chain-shaped lines indicate relatively poor physiological, urological, and reproductive functions. ➡

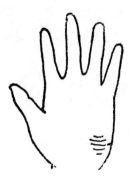

A weak wrist crease that is thin and broken with many blue veins on the surface of the wrist indicates a relatively weak reproductive function. It also shows a tendency toward gynecological disease. If the earth mound is also weak and thin, this is an even stronger indication of weak reproductive function. ⬅

11. Miscellaneous minor creases

If the lower part of the hypothenar eminence bulges and is crossed by transverse lines with more hand lines appearing after bathing, this may indicate a kidney disease. ➡

Transverse lines or arching, short lines on the hypothenar eminence are often seen in diabetes.

Many wrinkles on the lateral side of the hypothenar eminence are often seen in gastrointestinal disease.

➡

7
Chronology & the Palms

As mentioned in the introduction, one of the traditional examinations of the hand in Chinese palmistry is the determination of not just what has happened in the past or what is happening now but what is to come in the future. In medicine in general and in Chinese medicine in particular, one is always hoping to prevent disease before it arises. Therefore, if one could predict what is likely to occur in the future and then take steps to forestall that if it is negative, this would be a great boon. There are two basic ways of determining chronology in the hand in Chinese medical palmistry. The first has to do with dominant and passive hands and the second has to do with the lines on the palm.

Dominant & Passive Hands

The dominant hand is the hand that the person uses most often and is the most dexterous with. In most people, the right hand is the dominant hand. However, if a person is left-handed, then their left hand is their dominant hand. The passive hand is the less used, less dexterous hand. That means the left hand for a right-handed person and the right hand for a left-handed person.

According to Terence Dukes, the relationship between the dominant and passive hands is like that of a seed to a flower. The passive hand represents the matrix from which the person has developed. Thus Western palmists refer to this as the family hand. The passive hand, therefore, indicates in Chinese medical terms one's former heaven essence or *xian tian zhi jing*. Also called one's prenatal essence in English, this is one's inherited predisposition and constitution received from their mother and father at the moment of conception. Conversely, the dominant or active hand represents the latter heaven or postnatal development, which has occurred based on that original foundation. Thus, one can say that the passive hand indicates one's latent structural potential, while one's active hand shows one's current condition of physiological homeostasis.

Chronology & the Lines on the Palms

The lines on the palms relate to many different aspects of a person's being. They can indicate particular organs or physiological functions. They can indicate specific areas of the body. They can also indicate time. In general, one can divide any of the four most important lines into four sections. These four lines are the earth, human, and heaven lines and the jade column crease. These four sections are youth, young adulthood, middle age, and old age. Beginning with the flow of qi of each crease, one can then assign in order these four equal segments of each line.

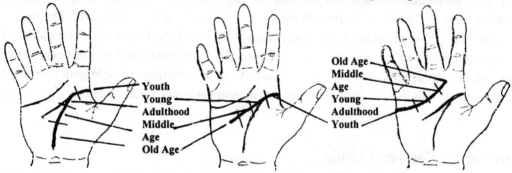

This method is not infallible and should be tempered by both common sense and corroboration by events in the subject's life. In some cases and especially with the jade column crease, a line may not fill out the entirety of its potential position. In other words it may end prematurely. In the case of the jade column line, one should determine age by the last method given below and not divide it into the four periods of life.

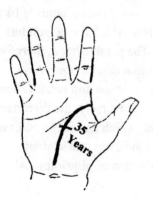

As an extension of this method, one can attempt to determine a particular year via the following method. If the average life span is 70 years, then the mid-point on a line corresponds to approximately 35 years of age. If one divides the two resulting sections in two again, one then will get the approximate positions of 17 and 52 years of age. By dividing these sections in half over and over again, one can, in theory, get down to individual years on a line. However, this method only really works on the major and minor earth lines, *i.e.*, the earth crease and the jade column crease.

←

As another rule of thumb, one can say that the point where the jade column crease crosses the human crease corresponds to 35 years of age on both lines. ➜

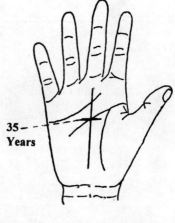

35 – –
Years

Because any given line may mean any of a number of things, one should not always read indications of time into appearances of and on the lines. For instance, an island halfway down the earth crease may correspond to something that occurred or will occur at middle age. It may also signify an injury or abnormality in the lower thoracic region of the spine or in the stomach. In other words, what it means is variable and dependent upon the actual experience and predisposition of the individual.

Book Two

Chinese Fingernail Diagnosis

1
Introduction to Chinese Fingernail Diagnosis

Fingernail diagnosis is a method of diagnosing disease of the body and its viscera and bowels and of assessing the degree of pathology by observing the state of qi and blood reflected in the color and luster of the ten fingernails. Clinical experience in China confirms that observation of the fingernails can help in early diagnosis and may also indicate the tendency of the disease. It can also disclose an otherwise hidden or insidious disease. By knowing the degree of pathological change reflected in the fingernail and by observing these changes in the disease condition, one can use fingernail diagnosis to aid in subsequent decisions regarding appropriate treatment.

Origins of Chinese Fingernail Diagnosis

TCM practitioners often look at the veins on the index fingers of children under three years old instead of palpating their pulses. In addition, TCM pediatricians routinely inspect the color of infants' fingernails to gauge heat and cold. In the past, it was recorded that the severity of a disease can be assessed by pressing the patient's fingernail until it turns white and then releasing it. If the nail bed returns to red, then the illness may be cured even if its chronic. However, if the nail bed does not return to its original red state, even an acute illness may be hard to treat.

In antiquity, the *Nei Jing (Inner Classic)* recorded that "black fingernails show death." Today, the textbook *Zhen Duan Xue (A Definitive Study of Diagnostics),* used in many TCM colleges also discusses diagnosing by the fingernail. It states, "If the lower half of the surface of the fingernail looks like frosted glass and the upper half looks red and brownish red," this is a kidney disease. Thus it is clear that fingernail diagnosis has its roots in Chinese antiquity although even modern Chinese medical textbooks recommend it and validate its usefulness. However, the system of fingernail diagnosis presented in this book is that of Wang Wen-hua and the indications are taken from Wang's book *Zhi Jia Zhen Bing (The Fingernails in the Diagnosis of Disease)*.

The Differences Between Chinese Medical Palmistry & Fingernail Diagnosis

Dr. Wang takes some pains in asserting that Chinese medical palmistry and her system of fingernail diagnosis are quite distinct. She points out that, although Chinese medical palmistry is based on observation of the hand, palm, and fingers, including the fingernails, it differs from fingernail diagnosis in three ways: First,its purpose is somewhat different. Palmistry seeks to identify tendencies toward disease but is not as good at identifying actual, present pathology. Fingernail diagnosis, on the other hand, seeks to distinguish specific pathologies of the viscera and bowels.

Secondly, its method is different. Chinese medical palmistry mainly observes the shape of the nails and color of the nail roots. Fingernail diagnosis looks at the shape, location, and color of the signs of the qi and blood appearing on the fingernail.

Thirdly, its diagnostic range is different. As mentioned above, Chinese medical palmistry studies the relationship between the fingernails and the tendency toward pathology. However, it also includes the relationship of the hand to personality, disposition, and psychological make-up. Fingernail diagnosis only studies the relationship between the nails and disease.

Be that as it may, Dr. Wang's fingernail diagnosis can be incorporated into Chinese medical palmistry. In this case, Dr. Wang's system of fingernail reading is simply an elaborate and refined method for observing and reading the signs that manifest in the fingernails.

Fingernail Diagnosis & Bioholography

As we have seen in Book One, bioholographic theory states that the human body is an organic whole. This means that there is a relationship between the whole and the parts such that the whole is reflected in every part. In other words, each part includes the information of the whole. Therefore, within the human body, every semi-independent part is, in sense, a miniature of the whole.

The ten fingernails are such semi-independent parts of the whole. Hence, according to the above theory, they include or reflect information from the whole body. Based on clinical experience, it has been found that when the palm is cupped with the ten fingernails facing each other, the distribution of qi and blood symbols on the nails is similar to a human fetus or homunculus.

With the nails held in this position, the near extremity of the fingernail corresponds to the dorsum of the body and the far extremity corresponds to the ventral side of the body. The thumbnail then corresponds to the head and neck. The index finger corresponds to the chest, back, hands, and elbows. The middle finger corresponds to the abdomen and low back. Because the viscera and bowels are mainly contained within the abdomen, they mainly reflect on the middle finger also. The hips and knees are reflected on the ring fingernail. Then the feet and ankles are reflected on the small fingernail. The two sides or sets of fingernails are symmetrical and together they reflect the human body's bioholographic image. ➜

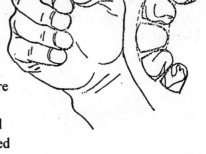

Fingernail Diagnosis & Microcirculation

In general, microcirculation refers to the microangium, meaning the blood circulation between the arterioles and venules. In a broader sense, it also includes lymphokinesis. It is the canal system that affects blood gases, the transport of nutrition, and the excretion of wastes. Different tissues and organs of the body have different capillary structures, but the basic functions of these are similar.

Since the 1950s, both research and clinical evaluation of microcirculation have proven that changes in microcirculation and blood rheology are invaluable in the discrimination of disease and in the guiding of treatment. Fingertip microcirculation is just one part of the general microcirculation. The capillaries of the nail fold are plentiful and very sensitive to changes in the body.

Microcirculation is what enables fingernail diagnosis. This is because all the main diseases of the different systems of the organism manifest pathologically in either local or systemic changes in microcirculation. Thus clinically it is useful to observe both the nail fold and bulbar conjunctiva microcirculation. Both of these can assist in clinical diagnosis. For instance, coronary heart disease, cerebral disease, pulmonary heart disease, epidemic encephalitis, and acute abdominal disease all show changes in microcirculation. In fact, microcirculation reflects changes in disease condition more than blood pressure, respiration, and pulse rate.

2
The Magic Square on the Fingernails

In order to observe, compare, and distinguish the qi and blood signs on the nail, one must have some way of mapping out the nail. The following method is called the nine divisions or magic square method.

In the nine divisions method, the nail is divided into nine equal parts. Thus the nail corresponds to the so-called magic square. This is a very ancient Chinese numerological representation with magical or at least mystical implications. It is a square made up of nine smaller squares, three to a side. Each square within the nine corresponds to one of the numerals from 1-9 and also to one of the

4	9	2
3	5	7
8	1	6

eight trigrams of the *Yi Jing (Classic of Change)*. It is called magic because no matter how one adds up the numerical correspondences of any three squares in a row, they always total 15.

The diagram and table below show these correspondences. However, in Chinese fingernail diagnosis, the choice of a nine-fold division does not have any further diagnostic implications as it does in eight trigram palmistry.

The Relationship Between Nine Locations and Eight Hexagrams

Locations	6	1	8	3	4	9	2&5	7
Diagrams	*Qian*	*Kan*	*Gen*	*Zhen*	*Sun*	*Li*	*Kun*	*Dui*
Images	Heaven	Water	Mountain	Thunder	Wind Wood	Fire	Earth	March Pond

In order to make this system easier to immediately remember for Westerners and especially Western health care practitioners, these ancient *ba gua* names have been replaced with anatomical descriptions. Therefore these anatomical sections may be referred to as:

1. the radial side near extremity
2. the radial side middle position
3. the radial side far extremity
4. the central near extremity
5. the central middle position
6. the central far extremity
7. the ulnar side near extremity
8. the ulnar side middle position
9. the ulnar side far extremity

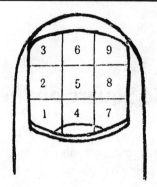

Right hand fingernail, nine division regional names

It is also possible to divide each of the above boxes into another nine boxes, thus arriving at a total of 81 small divisions of each fingernail. In this case, each smaller division of the main nine divisions are all similarly named. Thus one can speak of the ulnar side near extremity division of the central far extremity section, the radial side near extremity of the ulnar side far extremity, and so on.

Although it may sometimes be advantageous to use the anatomical precision of 81 divisions of the nail, in locating the signs described in the following chapters, 9 basic divisions are usually enough.

3
Qi & Blood Signs

Qi and blood signs refer to the location, shape, color, and luster of the qi and blood reflected on the fingernails. Because these signs are made by changes in the microcirculation under the nails, Dr. Wang calls them blood qi signs. In other words, by observing these signs produced by the blood, one can understand the state of both the qi and blood. This is because the qi and blood are inseparably interrelated. Nonetheless, because "blood qi signs" sounds awkward and unusual in English, we have referred to qi and blood signs from here on.

It is a basic tenet of Chinese fingernail diagnosis that various pathological changes and the degree of their severity are reflected by particular forms and their qualities reflected in the fingernail. This means that certain shapes correspond to certain diseases. These shapes are not fixed but can change over time, thus reflecting the progression or regression of the disease state with which they correspond. There are three basic criteria for interpreting these shapes in the nails. They are the shape itself, their color and luster, and their location.

1. Fingernail Sign Shapes

The qi and blood signs seen on the fingernails vary in size and shape. The different shapes that are identified in fingernail diagnosis are the round, semicircular, oval, crescent moon, dumbbell, strip, hook, splayed, triangular, and cone shapes. Other sign shapes are the dot, line, flake, stick, mist, and wave shapes.

In addition, there are variations that must be taken into account even within the same shape. For instance, the size of a shape is related to the range of the pathological change with which it is associated. Differences in same-shaped signs are often related to the clarity of the signs as well as to the age, profession, and habits of the individual.

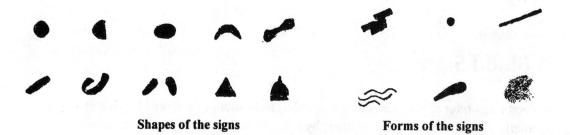

Shapes of the signs   **Forms of the signs**

In general, different diseases are associated with different shaped signs. However, it is possible for different diseases to manifest the same shaped sign, while sometimes the same disease may reflect different shaped signs. For example, in hepatomegaly or splenomegaly, the sign shape is either cone-like or triangular. The difference is that the former shape manifests on the right ring finger, while the latter shape appears on the left ring finger. Another example is coronary heart disease. Most of its sign shapes are triangular. Nevertheless, it can also manifest as an oval, a crescent moon, or a long strip shape. However, all these signs are located on the ulnar side of the left middle finger.

In many illnesses, if the disease is not cured, the sign on the fingernail will not disappear either. Only when the cure is complete will the fingernail sign disappear. In addition, some signs disappear completely, while others do not. The sign for a decayed tooth will disappear completely after it has been removed, and the same is true for duodenal bulbar ulcer. However, in case of focal calcification occurring in pulmonary tuberculosis, the sign of a round, dot shape will stay on the index fingernail for a long time. The only change is that its purplish-red color becomes a light grey. Also, if an ulcer is removed surgically, its sign can still be seen as a white, linear shape.

2. Color & Luster

Color and luster are the external manifestation of the flourishing of the qi and blood of the viscera and bowels. Hence the color and luster of the signs in the fingernail usually reflect the degree of pathological change and changes in a disease's progression or regression.

Color and luster are related, yet there are also differences between them. Color refers to hue, while luster refers to sheen or gloss. The common colors seen in qi and blood signs in the fingernails are red, light red, purplish-red, purplish-black, black, yellow, light yellow, white, and gray. Luster in fingernail diagnosis can be described as flourishing, smooth, bright, dull, and withered.

In TCM there is the saying that: "Excessive yellow becomes red; excessive red becomes purple; excessive purple becomes green; excessive green becomes black; and complete black is difficult to cure." This saying implies that colors reflected on the surface change as a disease progresses. Therefore, color is an indication of a disease's acute or chronic condition. Thus, in acute conditions, the corresponding fingernail sign's color and luster are bright red or purplish-red. During recovery or if the condition is stable, the corresponding sign's color becomes light red. And when a disease is severe, the sign's color may become either purple or black.

For example, the sign for gastritis during latent periods typically appears on the radial side far extremity of the right middle finger as a strip-like shape that is light red in color. If the gastritis becomes acute, then the color of this sign becomes bright red or purplish-red. Similar changes occur with the progression and regression of other diseases.

Clinically, a sign's color and luster can have special meaning for diagnosing certain types of diseases. The signs for myocardial infarction and cirrhosis are usually dark purple or black, whereas the sign for diabetes is a white color.

A sign's color and luster are also helpful in distinguishing between diseases. Both chronic colitis and constipation manifest a mist-shaped sign located at the near extremity of the radial side of the right middle fingernail. However, chronic colitis appears as a light red color, while constipation manifests as a light gray color. Thus these two diseases are only differentiated by the color of their corresponding shape.

3. Location of Signs

Most diseases only reflect signs on one spot on the fingernails in a fairly stable manner. Thus different diseases reflect signs in different locations on the fingernails. In coronary heart disease and hypertrophy of the thoracic vertebrae, the former's sign is located on the ulnar side of the left middle fingernail, while the latter's sign is located on the ulnar side of the right middle fingernail. According to TCM theory, both chronic bronchitis and asthma relate to the upper body and lungs. However, in fingernail diagnosis, their locations are different. Chronic bronchitis is reflected on the far extremity of the radial side of the index fingernail, while asthma is reflected on the near extremity of the radial side of the index fingernail.

It is also possible for different diseases to reflect at the same location on the fingernails if these diseases are located in the same general area of the body. In laryngopharyngitis and periarthritis of the shoulder, the signs of both diseases manifest on the far extremity of the radial side of the index fingernail, and the shapes of their signs are also the same. The only difference is that one or more signs can also be seen on the thumbnail in the case of laryngopharyngitis. This is because the involvement of the nasal passages occurs higher up in the body and thus manifests also on the thumb. Therefore, even though these two diseases manifest signs on the far extremity of the radial side of the index fingernail, they can still be distinguished.

Some diseases can have two, three, or even more signs, each appearing at two, three, or more locations on the fingernails. For instance, pancreatitis manifests as a semicircular-shaped sign on the left ring fingernail. It also manifests as a semicircular or oval-shaped sign on the left middle fingernail. At the same time, it further manifests a splay-shaped sign on the right ring fingernail. Persons with latent pancreatitis have all three of these signs in a light red color. When the pancreatitis flares up, these three signs then become bright red. Therefore, when diagnosing this disease, one needs to observe all three fingernails.

Some diseases can have a sign or signs at either one or two locations. With premature heartbeat, most patients' have dot-shaped signs on their left middle fingernail. Yet in other patients with this same condition, dot-shaped signs may simultaneously appear on the left index fingernail.

There is also another phenomenon that is seen in clinical practice, which should be noted. In every pathological change occurring in tissue or organs located on a particular side of the body, a sign appears on a fingernail of the same side. This means that a left-sided pathological change appears on a fingernail of the left side, and a right-sided pathological change appears on a fingernail of the right side. If pathological changes occur bilaterally, then there will be signs on the fingernails also occurring bilaterally.

For instance, in migraine, the sign of a left-sided headache appears on the far extremity of the ulnar side of the left thumbnail. Conversely, the sign of a right-sided headache appears on the far extremity of the ulnar side of the right thumbnail. While the sign for a bilateral headache appears on both thumbnails-Chronic nephritis is similar. Its sign on the left ring fingernail reflects the left kidney, while its sign on the right ring fingernail reflects the right kidney. If signs are seen on both hands, this indicates a pathological change in both kidneys.

4
Basic Hand Techniques in Fingernail Diagnosis

The signs that one reads in Chinese fingernail diagnosis are not necessarily apparent by simply looking at the nails in a static position. Often these fingernail signs appear only after manipulating the fingertip and putting varying amounts and directions of pressure on the nail itself, thus engorging and emptying the venules and arterioles making up the microcirculation. These techniques of massaging and pressing the fingertips and nails are referred to as *shou fa* or hand techniques. These hand techniques help improve one's discernment of the signs in the nail and thus are an important part of Chinese fingernail diagnosis.

To begin with, when observing the fingernail, it is best if the patient holds their hand out, slightly bent at the palm with the fingers extended naturally. First, one should observe whether the fingernails are complete, damaged, or stained. This determines if the nails can be validly judged. Then, using one's thumb and index finger, one should hold both sides of the distal phalanx (*i.e.*, the last joint) of any one of the patient's fingers, stabilizing the fingertip. Next, using the thumb and index finger of the other hand, the practitioner should hold both sides of the fingernail.

Holding the patient's finger one can then apply the following techniques as necessary: kneading, twisting, pushing, squeezing, pressing, throwing down, and rubbing. After having applied these hand techniques to the finger under examination, one stops and observes, compares, and distinguishes each qi and blood sign's shape, location, color, and luster. ➡

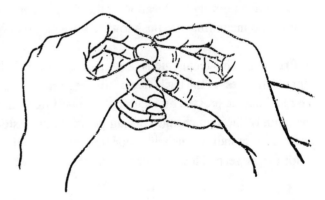

1. Kneading: This is the most basic of the hand techniques used in Chinese fingernail diagnosis. The practitioner begins by holding both sides of the patient's fingernail with a thumb and index finger. Then one kneads the soft tissue surrounding and the area of the fingernail itself. Generally, it is best to do this maneuver lightly. However, if the fingernails are excessively thick, in individuals who are weak with poor microcirculation, or in the aged, it is best to knead downward a little heavier in order to clearly observe the signs in the nails.

2. Twisting: This is also a basic hand technique used in Chinese fingernail diagnosis and is done at the same time as kneading. Move the thumb and index finger up and down in turn, twisting the fingernail. During this motion, the fingernail's qi and blood twist with it. Therefore signs reflecting particular diseases can manifest. The speed and strength of this twisting motion should be based on the need and the patient's condition.

3. Pushing: In this maneuver, the index finger, which was used to knead in the first hand technique, does not move. Rather the thumb is used to push forward. The thumb may also push to the left and forward, to the right and forward, or even in the opposite direction. Here one is looking to see if the qi and blood sign moves in the direction of the pushing. Generally, qi and blood signs cannot be moved, and even when they are able to be moved, only the color of the sign changes somewhat. This technique is used to determine the shape and location of the signs in the fingernail.

4. Squeezing: This technique is based on kneading. Use the thumb and index finger to squeeze toward the middle or to one side of the fingernail under observation. This maneuver is also used for determining the location of the sign. Squeezing can also be described as using the thumb and index finger to push toward the same spot on the nail.

5. Pressing: This technique is used in order to watch the color and luster of the qi and blood signs. One presses the back side of the fingernail by using either their thumb or index finger. The nail can be pressed by either one or two fingers at the same time. Generally speaking, only the color of the sign changes during pressing; the luster does not. In the aged, in those with anemia, or in individuals with poor fingertip microcirculation, during pressing, only a pale color can be seen. This is an important observation.

6. Throwing down: This hand technique involves throwing down the hand suddenly during kneading, squeezing, pushing, and pressing. Sometimes, one should let one finger suddenly go. At other times, one can let go of two fingers simultaneously. This technique aids in observing the recovery of the qi and blood and the relationship of adjacent signs as well as changes in color and luster. In other words, one can observe if the color and luster of a sign remain the same after being pressed then thrown down.

7. Rubbing: This technique is based on the location of the qi and blood sign. It is performed by rubbing the back side of the fingernail with the thumb or index finger. The purpose of this maneuver is to further distinguish and judge a sign if it is not clear. It is also used if the relationship of adjacent signs is not clear or when something is questionable.

8. Stopping: During the afore-mentioned techniques, once a sign if found, one should stop and observe it carefully. While stopping, it is best not to move from the original position. Only the angle of observation and direction should to be altered and adjusted in order to compare and differentiate the signs revealed.

These different techniques are not all used in any one examination. Rather they are employed on an as-needed basis.

5
The Ten Fingernails & Their Indications

According to TCM theory, the thumb pertains to the lung channel. The index finger pertains to the large intestine channel. The middle finger pertains to the pericardium channel. The ring finger pertains to the triple burner channel. The inner side of the small finger pertains to the heart, and its outer side pertains to the small intestine channel. That being said, in clinical practice, the disease areas reflected on different fingernails are not always related to the signs of pathological change of these related channels and network vessels. As stated previously, the ten fingernails taken as a whole can be seen as a homunculus.

Based on clinical experience, it has been found that the signs of particular diseases habitually appear on specific nails or on different regions of specific nails. These disease signs tend to be distributed on the nails based on their anatomical location. In other words, diseases of the lungs show signs on the index fingernail because, according to bioholographic theory, the index fingernail corresponds to the region of the chest in which the lungs are located. They do not show signs on the thumbnail even though that is where the lung channel terminates. Thus all the general indications below for the each of the ten fingernails are based on this map of a homunculus.

1. Thumbnails

In terms of their correspondences, the thumbnails of both hands are similar. Only their left and right directions are opposite. The thumbnails correspond to the head and neck region of the body. Therefore, commonly seen diseases manifesting signs on the thumbnails are upper respiratory infections, rhinitis, paranasal sinusitis, nasal polyps, laryngopharyngitis, tonsillitis, stomatitis, periodontitis, dental caries, otitis media, headache, including migraine, decreased vision, cervical lymphadenopathy, and brain tumors.

Right Thumbnail

133

2. Index fingernails

The index finger mainly reflects diseases in the upper burner, upper extremities, and some parts of the throat and the middle burner. The right index fingernail shows signs of diseases in the lungs, trachea, esophagus, breasts, chest and back, hand, elbow, shoulder, throat, and neck. Commonly seen diseases reflecting in these areas include acute and chronic bronchitis, bronchial asthma, pneumonia, pulmonary tuberculosis, pulmonary emphysema, pleurisy, esophagitis, esophageal cancer, laryngitis, mastitis and other breast diseases, cervical and thoracic hypertrophy of the vertebrae as well as hand and shoulder diseases.

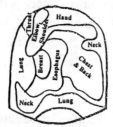 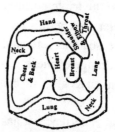

Diagnostic areas on the right index fingernail   **Diagnostic areas on the left index fingernail**

The left index fingernail reflects basically the same or similar diseases. However, the left and right directions are reversed. The left nail also manifests signs relating to heart disease with both high and low blood pressure being reflected at almost the same location as the heart.

3. Middle fingernails

The middle fingernail mainly reflects the middle burner as well as some upper and lower burner diseases. The right fingernail usually reflects pathological changes in the stomach, duodenum, diaphragm, liver, pancreas, kidney, lung and chest, waist, and large intestine.

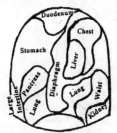 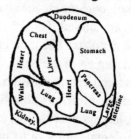

Diagnostic areas on the right middle fingernail   **Diagnostic areas on the left middle fingernail**

134

Commonly seen diseases showing signs on the middle fingernails include stomachache, chronic gastritis, stomach and duodenal ulcers, pyloric disease, inflammation of the diaphragmatic membrane, hepatomegaly, and kidney disease.

As with the above-mentioned fingernails, the left middle fingernail is basically the same as the right, but reversed. However, it may also show signs related to the heart. Commonly seen diseases manifesting signs on this fingernail, therefore, include coronary heart disease, myocarditis, tachycardia, premature heartbeat, aortic sclerosis, and left ventricular enlargement. Gastritis, pancreatitis, and diabetes are also reflected here.

4. Ring fingernails

The ring fingernail mainly reflects diseases in the lower burner and some diseases of the middle burner. The right ring fingernail, therefore, reflects pathological changes in the liver, gallbladder, pancreas, kidney, small and large intestines, bladder, reproductive organs, knees, and lumbar area. ➡

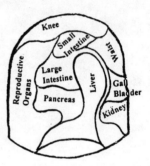

Commonly seen diseases manifesting on the right ring fingernail include hepatitis, cirrhosis of the liver, increase in transaminase, cholecystitis, pancreatitis, colitis, nephritis, rheumatic arthritis, and hypertrophy of the lumbar vertebrae as well as diseases of the anus.

The left ring fingernail mainly reflects pathological changes in the spleen, pancreas, uterus, urethra, vas deferens, vulva, uterus, and anus. ➡

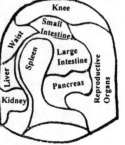

135

5. Small fingernail

Clinically, most of the diseases reflected on the small
fingernail are located below the knees, such as pain
in the heels and metatarsals. Occasionally diseases of
the prostate also manifest on the small fingernails.

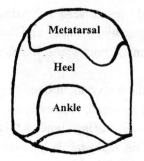

6
Specific Diseases & Chinese Fingernail Diagnosis

In this chapter, the clinical use of Chinese fingernail diagnosis is discussed and exemplified in relationship to a number of commonly seen diseases in clinical practice. The diseases presented in this chapter are all modern Western disease categories. Most of them are chronic and many of them are serious. In addition, almost all the diseases discussed involve some organic change in the diseased organ or body part. In other words, the majority of diseases discussed in this chapter showing obvious pathological signs in the fingernails are not simply functional diseases. This is significant since it underscores the types of conditions amenable to diagnosis by this method.

Under each disease category, the traditional Chinese disease name or names are listed. Because the traditional Chinese disease categories are not identical to modern Western ones, often a single modern Western disease is covered by more than one traditional Chinese disease. For instance, chronic colitis may be categorized in TCM as either diarrhea if there are primarily loose stools, as dysentery if there are many bowel movements per day, or as intestinal wind if there is hemafecia. Thus the several traditional Chinese names listed after each Western disease are not identical but are actually different diseases within TCM.

After identification of the traditional Chinese disease categories covering the Western disease under discussion, next comes a discussion of the TCM disease causes (*bing yin*) and disease mechanisms (*bing ji*) for each disease. This material is then usually summed up by stating which organs are primarily involved in each condition.

The diseases discussed in this chapter are primarily arranged by body part, beginning with diseases in the upper part of the body and descending in order to diseases of the lower part of the body. Thus the order of presentation of these diseases follows the order of their manifestation of signs on the fingernails from the thumb to the little finger. There are also a couple of diseases discussed, hypertension and diabetes, that are not easily localized in the body. Each disease is accompanied by one or more of Dr. Wang's case histories.

Diseases of the Head and Neck

1. Migraine

Migraine headaches are experienced by as much as 25% of all people at some time in their lives. The symptoms of migraine headaches are varied, but classical migraines are characterized by intense, usually one-sided pain, photophobia, possible tingling and paresthesia in the extremities or over one-half of the body, and nausea with possible vomiting. Therefore, in TCM, migraines are called one-sided headaches. Although, in TCM, there are a number of different types of migraines, such as those caused by invasion of external evils and those caused by internal damage affecting the viscera and bowels, the one bit of TCM theory all migraines have in common is that the head is the place where all yang gathers. The head is connected to all the qi and blood of five viscera and six bowels, and the fingernails reflect this.

Fingernail sign location: The far extremity of the ulnar side of the thumb

Fingernail sign shape: A slanting strip

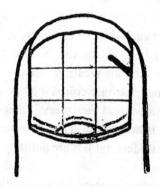

Fingernail sign color & luster: When a migraine is occurring, the color of its sign is bright red or purplish- red. When the condition is stable, that is to say, between migrainous attacks, the color of its sign is light red. ➔

Case 1: A 23-year-old male student came in on April 25, 1987. Dr. Wang first observed his fingernails and made her diagnosis, then listened to the patient's complaint. A slanting strip-like sign was observed on the far extremity of the ulnar side of his left thumbnail. It was a bright red color. Thus Dr. Wang's diagnosis was that a migraine was presently occurring. The patient stated, That is exactly what I have come in for. Please check to see whether I have anything growing in my brain. He also stated that he had had this disease for over 3 years, although no cause had previously been found.

The patient frequently took painkillers when a migraine was present. The migraines occurred mainly on the left side. He could not do anything because of the pain and felt very irritable. His main worry was that he might have a brain tumor. The patient was told that he had a migraine, not a tumor, and that the fingernail signs of these two diseases are different. After hearing this, the patient left relieved.

Case 2: A 45-year-old female physician came in on July 8, 1987, to have her fingernails diagnosed. A slanting strip-like sign was visible on the far extremity of the ulnar side of her right thumbnail. Its color was light red. Fingernail diagnosis showed that she had a history of migraines. The patient said that she had had migraines for over 20 years and that they occurred frequently. Three years ago, a definite diagnosis of vascular headache had been confirmed. Her electroencephalogram (EEG) was normal.

2. Dizziness

The diagnosis and treatment of dizziness in TCM is based on a couple of ancient sayings, Without vacuity, there is no dizziness, and Without phlegm, there is no dizziness. However, TCM channel theory relates dizziness to the liver. In clinical practice, this symptom is commonly caused by ascendant liver yang and insufficient kidney essence. In addition, phlegm and dampness may also intertwine and obstruct the flow of clear yang in the head. Further, due to qi and blood both being vacuous, there may not be enough clear yang to invigorate the clear portals or enough blood to nourish the sea of marrow. Based on the above several disease mechanisms, one can say that dizziness in TCM has to do with the liver, kidneys, spleen, and stomach (due to the spleen's being both the root of phlegm engenderment and the latter heaven engenderment of qi and blood). ➜

Fingernail sign location: The whole thumbnail or part of it

Fingernail sign shape: Misty or cloud-like shape

Fingernail sign color & luster: Light gray

Dizziness as manifesting on the thumbnail

139

Case 1: A 45-year-old female farmer came in on May 16, 1987. Dr. Wang first observed her fingernails and stated her diagnosis before listening to the patient's complaint. The surface of both of her thumbnails had a misty, strip-shaped sign that was a light gray color. The area was comparatively large. Dr. Wang's fingernail diagnosis was, therefore, dizziness that was presently occurring. The patient stated that she had been experiencing dizziness for the last 7-8 years. Sometimes it was light and other times it was more severe. The day before yesterday she had had it again. The reason for her dizziness was not clear.

Case 2: A 34-year-old male factory worker came in on March 25, 1987. He had been dizzy and was suspicious about having a brain tumor. He wanted to have his fingernails diagnosed. The surface of both thumbnails displayed mist-like signs that were a grayish-purple color. This means that dizziness is presently occurring. In addition to this, a slanted, strip-shaped sign could be seen on the far extremity of the ulnar side of both thumbnails. These signs were purplish red in color on the left hand and a dark purple color on the right. These signs meant that the headache was more severe on the right side. The patient was told that the sign of brain tumor could not be seen.

However, there was qi stagnation and blood stasis, which were comparatively severe. The dizziness could, therefore, possibly be caused by inhibition in the flow of qi and blood. The patient stated that he had been knocked down 2 years ago when he was riding a bicycle. He had felt very befuddled at that time, yet was all right after a few days of rest. After that, however, he had experienced dizziness and headaches. Occasionally he was symptom-free. In the last half year, the symptoms had become more severe and lasted longer. He typically felt fatigued and irritable.

The patient was treated with the following medicinals: Rhizoma Curcuma Zedorariae (*E Zhu*), Ramulus Cinnamoni (*Gui Zhi*), Fructus Ligustri Lucidi (*Nu Zhen Zi*), Herba Ecliptae Prostrae (*Han Lian Cao*), Radix Ligustici Wallichii (*Chuan Xiong*), Exocarpium Semenis Phaseoli Munginis (*Lu Dou Yi*), Fructus Viticis (*Man Jing Zi*), Rhizoma Corydalis Yanhusuo (*Yan Hu Suo*), and Herba Pycnostelmae Paniculati (*Xu Chang Jing*). Seven packets were administered in decoction.

When he returned, the patient stated that the symptoms of headache and dizziness had decreased and that he felt better. Fingernail diagnosis showed that the signs on both thumbnails had become lighter. The sign on the right thumbnail had become purplish-red, reduced from dark purple. His was told, therefore, to continue with the same treatment for another half month.

The third time he came in, the patient stated that his fingernail signs had essentially disappeared. The signs on the far extremity of the ulnar side of both thumbnails had all become light red. The patient was told to take the same formula for another month to secure the result.

3. Myopia (Nearsightedness)

Myopia, in TCM, is called can see near, fear far condition. It can be due to heart yang vacuity failing to vitalize the clear portals of the eyes. It can also be due to yin exuberance in which case, phlegm may obstruct the passage of clear yang to the eyes. Further, myopia can be due to liver/kidney vacuity. This means liver blood/kidney yin vacuity and, in this case, the eyes lose their nourishment and fluids. There are also the sayings, born to be nearsighted and excess looking damages the eyes. The first saying implies that nearsightedness may be congenital in some patients. The second saying means that nearsightedness may be the result of over-use of the eyes, as in excessive reading.

Fingernail sign location: The near extremity of the radial side of the thumbnail

Fingernail sign shape: Misty or cloud-like shape

Fingernail sign color & luster: Light gray

Myopia manifesting on the left thumbnail

Case: An 18-year-old female teacher came in on April 15, 1987. Dr Wang first diagnosed her by observing her fingernails and then listened to her complaint. The near extremity of the radial side of both thumbnails showed misty, cloud-like signs that were a light gray color. The sign color was deeper on her left hand than her right hand. Her diagnosis was decreased visual acuity, with nearsightedness of her left eye being more severe than the right. The patient stated that she had just had her eyes checked and her left eye was 500 degrees and her right, 250 degrees.

Note: The above qi and blood sign is only used in a general sense to indicate decreased visual acuity.

4. Glaucoma

Glaucoma, in TCM, is called green wind internal obstruction. It is called this because this disease's condition is urgent and sudden, changing like a wind. It is usually due to emotional depression constraining the flow of liver qi. This, in turn, transforms into fire, engendering internal wind that ascends to disturb the eyes. It can also be due to liver/kidney yin vacuity, qi and blood disharmony, and vacuity fire ascending to attack the eyes.

Fingernail sign location: The near extremity of the radial side of the thumbnail

Fingernail sign shape: Wave-like

Fingernail sign color & luster: Gray

Glaucoma manifesting on the left thumbnail)

Case: A 43-year-old female worker came in for fingernail diagnosis. A gray, wave-like sign was found on the near extremity of the radial side of her left thumbnail. She was told at once that she had glaucoma. The patient stated that this was also the definite diagnosis given her at the Western medical hospital.

5. Chronic rhinitis

In TCM, chronic rhinitis is referred to as deep source nasal congestion. Its main symptom is a chronically congested nose that cannot be relieved. Symptoms may include pusy nasal discharge caused by lung qi congestion and stagnation. The governing vessel stops at the lip and the kidneys are in charge of sneezing and the absorption of qi. Therefore, in general, chronic rhinitis is related to the lungs, kidneys, and governing vessel.

Fingernail sign location: The middle and far extremities of the central part of the thumbnail

Fingernail sign shape: A strip-like shape

Fingernail sign color & luster: Light red between flare-ups; bright red or purplish-red during acute episodes

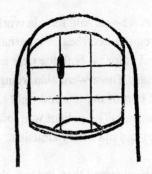

Chronic rhinitis manifesting on the right thumbnail

Case: A 35-year-old female technician came in on Sept 18, 1986, for a check-up. Through observing her nails, it was found that there was a straight, bright red strip on the middle and far extremities of the central part of her right thumbnail. Dr. Wang's diagnosis was chronic rhinitis, which was currently present. The patient admitted that she had had this condition for 7-8 years and it was currently a problem. Her symptoms were nasal congestion with diminished sense of smell and a yellow nasal discharge. She also complained of dizziness and headache.

6. Chronic maxillary sinusitis

Maxillary sinusitis is the most common among the varieties of nasal sinusitis. In TCM, it is also referred to as deep source nasal congestion. Symptoms of this condition include a thick, runny nasal discharge, which, at times, has a foul odor. Severe cases may also be called brain leakage and brain flooding. This disease is often seen in vacuity states with dampness. In that case, it is due to lung and spleen vacuity. Chronic maxillary sinusitis is also commonly due to coldness, phlegm, and inability of pure yang to ascend as well as to debility of the righteous qi.

Fingernail sign location: The central part of the thumbnail

Fingernail qi sign shape: Dot, strip, triangular, and/or cone-like shapes

Fingernail sign color & luster: Light red

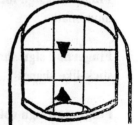

Chronic maxillary sinusitis manifesting on the right thumbnail

Case: A 42-year-old female worker came in on October 8, 1987, complaining of a tight chest and irregular heartbeat. Fingernail diagnosis revealed a single round dot-shaped sign with a light red color on both the near and far extremities of the central part of the left middle fingernail. There were also triangular and cone-shaped signs on the near extremity of the central part of the left and right thumbnails. The former was light red and the latter was purplish-red. The patient was told that she had intermittent premature heartbeat (*i.e.*, extra systole) and maxillary sinusitis.

The patient stated that, indeed, she did have a premature heartbeat. This had also been disclosed by electrocardiograph (EKG). She did not know, however, that she had maxillary sinusitis and had never been checked for it. However, she did experience a dry sensation in her nasal cavity, nasal congestion, and a nasal discharge from the back of her nostril. Later, a suggested X-ray examination described her condition thus: Decrease in transparency of the two maxillary sinuses with thickened mucous membranes. This X-ray thus confirmed pathological changes in the maxillary sinuses.

7. Nasopharyngeal carcinoma

One of the key symptoms of nasopharyngeal carcinoma is a thick, yellow mucus that runs from the nasal aperture. If not cured, there is a dripping, foul-smelling, bloody discharge that runs down from the nose accompanied by dizziness and headache. This demonstrates that *jue yin* phlegm has formed and invaded upward into the nasopharynx, or, in other words, ascendant liver yang has drafted phlegm up to brew
in the otherwise clear portal of the nose.

Fingernail sign location: The central part of the thumbnail

Fingernail sign shape: Strip, hook, dot, and/or stick-like shapes

Fingernail sign color & luster: Black or purplish-black

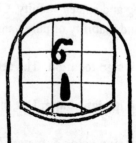

Nasopharyngeal carcinoma manifesting on the right thumbnail

Case 1: A 48-year-old male came in on March 31, 1988. A check of his nails revealed a black colored, stick-shaped sign surrounded by purplish-red color on the near extremity of the central part of his right thumbnail. Another purplish-black, hook-shaped sign was seen on the middle and far extremity. Dr. Wang diagnosed this man as suffering from nasopharyngeal carcinoma. After this diagnosis, the patient confirmed that he been diagnosed with this disease in July of 1987. He had had radiation therapy and he was coming in to be reexamined. A CAT scan showed that the mucous membrane at the bottom of his nose had thickened. He also had right-sided peripheral facial paralysis.

Case 2: A 63-year-old male came in on December 21, 1987, to have an outpatient service. A check of his fingernails found that there was a purplish-black, dot-shaped sign on the middle and far extremities of the central part of the right thumbnail. A purplish-red, dot-shaped sign at the near extremity was also seen. Dr. Wang stated that a diagnosis of nasopharyngeal carcinoma was possible. Afterwards, the patient went and had tests that confirmed that he did, in fact, have nasopharyngeal carcinoma.

8. Chronic laryngitis

Chronic laryngitis, in TCM is called throat *bi*. Clinically, its symptoms are mainly chronic throat dryness and a sensation of a foreign body in the throat. It is due to chronic shortage of kidney fluids and fire scorching upward. This fire disperses the lungs and smokes the throat. Yin vacuity throat *bi* is mainly due to liver/kidney yin vacuity. Yang vacuity throat *bi* is usually due to yin detriment affecting yang.

Fingernail sign location: The far extremity of the thumbnail

Fingernail sign shape: A dot

Fingernail sign color & luster: Light red between occurrences; purplish-red when present

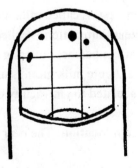

Chronic laryngitis manifesting on the right thumbnail

Case: A 31-year-old male worker came in on November 30, 1986, because of a sensation of obstruction in his throat. A nail check found that four, purplish-red, dot-shape signs were visible on the far extremity of his right thumbnail, with of these two on the radial side of the far extremity. The other two dots appeared separate in the middle and on the ulnar side of the far extremity. Dr. Wang's fingernail diagnosis of this patient was chronic laryngitis. The TCM term is plum pit qi. The patient was then asked about his medical history. In fact, he did have a sensation of a foreign body in his throat, which he could neither swallow nor spit out. This sensation had nothing to do with food, and he had no difficulty eating either soft or hard food. He was treated many times by Western methods with unfavorable results.

The treatment principles Dr. Wang employed in the treatment of this patient were to rectify the qi, quicken the blood, and nourish yin. He was thus prescribed the following medicinals: Pericarpium Trichosanthis Kirlowii (*Gua Lou Pi*), Radix Trichosanthis Kirlowii (*Tian Hua Fen*), Radix Glenniae Littoralis (*Sha Shen*), Calyx Viridis Prunus Makino (*Lu E Mei*), Radix Salviae Miltiorrhizae (*Dan Shen*). Seven packets were administered in decoction.

Seven days later, the patient returned. He stated that, after 3 days, the disease had decreased markedly. After all 7 packets, he was basically cured. A few more packets were required to secure the result. A nail check found that the color of the four dot-shaped signs on the right thumbnail had changed from purplish-red to light red.

9. Tonsillitis

Tonsillitis, in TCM, is called milk moth. Its main symptoms are sore throat and swelling of the tonsils. Acute inflammation is called wind heat milk moth. This condition is called milk moth because the white patches covering the tonsils look both milky and like a moth sitting on the bark of a tree. Acute milk moth is usually due to the lung/stomach heat toxins, while chronic milk moth is related to yin vacuity of the lungs and kidneys.

Fingernail sign location: The near extremity of the radial side of the thumbnail

Fingernail sign shape: A semicircle

146

Fingernail sign color & luster: Chronic conditions manifest a light red; acute conditions, bright red or purplish-red. ➜

Tonsillitis manifesting on the right thumbnail

Case: An 11-year-old female student came in for a nail check. A semicircular-shaped sign which was purplish-red was found on the near extremity of the radial side of both of her thumbnails. Dr. Wang's diagnosis was tonsillitis that was presently occurring. The mother stated that her daughter had already been diagnosed with tonsillitis at the Western medical hospital and was receiving penicillin injections.

10. Dental caries

Tooth decay in TCM is called tooth parasites. It is due to *yang ming* exuberant heat with the teeth being eroded by parasites. A branch of the foot *yang ming* goes to the upper teeth, while a branch of hand *yang ming* goes to the lower teeth. If the marrow is insufficient or the vessels of the *yang ming* are vacuous, then different diseases of the teeth can occur. Therefore, the strength and vacuity of the kidney qi also influence the health of the teeth.

Fingernail sign location: The near extremity of the radial side of the thumbnail

Fingernail sign shape: A strip

Fingernail sign color & luster: Light red

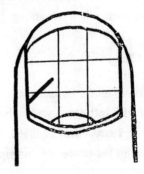

Dental caries manifesting on the right thumbnail

147

Case: A 26-year-old female worker came to see Dr. Wang on March 15, 1987. A nail check found a purplish-red, slanted, strip-shaped sign on the near extremity of the radial side of her right thumbnail. She was, therefore, diagnosed as suffering from a decayed tooth. She said that she did have such a decayed tooth and it had been filled, yet she was still in pain.

Upper Burner Diseases

1. Bronchitis

In TCM, bronchitis is categorized under cough and phlegm rheum. It is divided into two types: acute and chronic. Coughing is its main symptom. Some cases are accompanied by dyspnea. Bronchitis is mainly related to the lungs. It is commonly caused by lung qi congestion and obstruction that is not diffusing and downbearing. In addition, the stomach and intestines may accumulate heat, and this heat may steam the lungs.
Another cause is lung/kidney yin vacuity.

Fingernail sign location: The far extremity of the radial side of the index fingernail

Fingernail sign shape: A slanting strip

Fingernail sign color & luster: Light red between episodes; when occurring, bright red

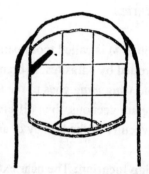

Bronchitis manifesting on the right index fingernail

Case 1: A 70-year-old female came in on May 21, 1986. A nail check found a slanted, strip-shaped sign with left down and right up. Its color was bright red and it was located at the middle and far extremities of the radial side of her right index fingernail. A purplish red dot was also seen in the center of this sign. This indicated that bronchitis was currently occurring.

The patient was then asked about her medical history. She stated that half a month ago she had had a flu. She still had a cough, a chest oppression, and shortness of breath. She also coughed up phlegm. This phlegm was worse in the morning. Dr. Wang instructed this patient to have immediate chest fluoroscopy. This showed that the veins of the lungs had deepened, primarily in the right upper lung. Nothing else was abnormal.

Case 2: A 36-year-old male came in on September 18, 1986. A nail check found a slanted, strip-shaped sign with left up and right down. It was a bright red color and located on the far extremity of the radial side of his left index fingernail. Dr. Wang's diagnosis of this patient was tracheitis, primarily on the left side. The patient stated that, half a month ago, he had had a flu and still coughed. He had been to the hospital the day before and had, in fact, been diagnosed with tracheitis.

2. Bronchial asthma

Bronchial asthma, in TCM, is categorized as wheezing and dyspnea. There are two types: wheezing condition (*xiao*) and panting condition (*chuan*). Its main signs are short, rapid breathing with a wheezing sound in the throat, chest oppression, obstructed breathing, and inability to lie flat. Its causes are very complicated. Phlegm and qi may join and thus obstruct, blocking the airways. The lungs may lose their ability to diffuse and downbear. Wheezing and dyspnea are also divided into vacuity and repletion. The *Nei Jing (Inner Classic)* says, The *tai yin* and *yang ming* are the channels of dyspnea and the lungs and kidneys are the viscera of dyspnea.

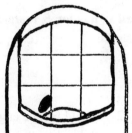

Fingernail sign location: The near extremity of the radial side of the index fingernail

Fingernail sign shape: An oval

Fingernail sign color & luster: Light red or light gray

Bronchial asthma manifesting on the right index fingernail

Case: A 38-year-old female came in to the hospital on March 15, 1988 because of chest oppression, nervousness, and palpitations. A checkup revealed that nothing was wrong with her heart. However, Dr. Wang could see an oval-shaped sign on the near extremity of the radial side of both her left and right index fingernails. These were a light red color. Her diagnosis was, therefore, asthma. On listening to her lungs, a wheezing sound could be heard in the upper right lung. She admitted that she had had asthma for 20 years.

3. Pneumonia

Pneumonia, in TCM, is variously called lung wind heat dyspnea, lung heat dyspnea and cough, lung block dyspnea and cough, etc. It belongs to the category of warm/heat diseases. Its main symptoms are fever, cough, and difficult breathing. Warm evils rise upward and first offend the lungs. If the lung qi is vacuous and the righteous cannot overcome these evils, both cause the lungs to lose their clearing and depurating function, thus causing blockage and depression with no diffusion. Exuberant phlegm heat may also congest and obstruct the airways. Thus pathological changes associated with this disease are mainly in the lungs.

Fingernail sign location: The near extremity of the central part of the index fingernail

Fingernail sign shape: Crescent, cone, and/or slice-like shapes

Fingernail sign color & luster: Bright red or purplish-red

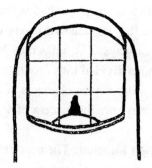

Pneumonia manifesting on the right index fingernail

Case: A 32-year-old female engineer came in on March 5, 1987, to have a nail check. A slice-shaped sign with bright red color was observed on the near extremity of the central part of her right index fingernail. She was diagnosed immediately with pneumonia and was told that she required immediate treatment. She stated that she had been coughing for half a month and was still ill. A week ago, she had had a fluoroscopy examination of her chest but nothing was found. Dr. Wang suggested that she have another. The result of this second test was the appearance of a speckle-shaped, blurry shadow on the right upper lung. She was given both Chinese and modern Western medicine.

4. Pulmonary tuberculosis (TB)

In TCM, pulmonary tuberculosis is called lung consumption, vacuity taxation, and consumption. Its main symptoms are cough, hemoptysis, tidal fever, night sweats, and emaciation. The site of the disease is in the lungs, but it is also related to the spleen and kidneys. The spleen is the source of engenderment and transformation. If the spleen is vacuous, water and grain essence qi cannot be transported upward to the lungs. This can cause insufficiency of lung fluids. The kidneys are the former heaven or prenatal root. If kidney essence is depleted, then vacuity fire may harass above, causing lung fluids to be scorched.

Fingernail sign location: The near extremity of the index fingernail

Fingernail sign shape: A round dot

Fingernail sign color & luster: Purplish-red or bright red

Pulmonary tuberculosis manifesting on the right index fingernail

Case: A 35-year-old female farmer came in on December 29, 1986 due to cough, weight loss, night sweats, and irregular menstruation. One purplish red, round, dot-shaped sign was seen on the near extremity of the radial side of her right index fingernail with bright red lines radiating around it. The patient was diagnosed with pulmonary tuberculosis and Dr. Wang suggested that she have this diagnosis confirmed at a Western medical hospital. A week later, the patient returned for treatment and stated that the hospital's diagnosis was infiltration stage pulmonary tuberculosis in the upper left lung.

Addendum: Lung calcification spot

After pulmonary tuberculosis has been cured, there may remain a calcification spot in the lung as a trace of this disease. The sign of this in the fingernail is the same shape in the same location as TB, only its color is light gray.

Case: A 48-year-old female worker came in on February 20, 1986. Two round dots were found on the near extremity of the central part and the ulnar side of her right index fingernail. The former was larger than the latter and both were a light gray color. The patient stated that when she was young, her father had had lung disease and that she had had close contact with him. When she had a fluoroscopic examination because of illness in 1973, two calcification spots had been found in her lungs.

5. Lung cancer

In TCM, primary cancer of the lung is believed to be caused when first there is damage of the righteous qi and subsequently there is invasion of the lungs by evil toxins. Among the four causes of illness, *i.e.*, qi, blood, phlegm, and food, lung cancer mostly pertains to the qi. If lung qi becomes depressed, the lung may lose command of diffusion and downbearing. The qi mechanism is thus inhibited and qi and blood do not flow easily. Hence the vessels and network vessels are obstructed and hindered. In this case, clinically there will be the appearance of symptoms such as coughing, chest pain, hemoptysis, and fever. The progression of this disease also has something to do with the location of the pathology. The central type of lung cancer appears early, while the peripheral type appears comparatively later.

Fingernail sign location: The near extremity of the index fingernail

Fingernail sign shape: A dot, strip, stick, and/or oval

Fingernail sign color & luster: Black, purplish-black, purplish-red, yellow

Lung cancer manifesting on the right index fingernail

Case: A 75-year-old male retired worker came in on March 17, 1988. One purple-black, oval-shaped sign a short distance from the near extremity of the central part of the index fingernail was seen. There was a light yellow color around it. Another black, dot-shaped sign was seen at the near extremity of the ulnar side of the same index fingernail. The patient stated that a month ago he had begun to cough suddenly and this became worse as time went by. After tests in the hospital, he was diagnosed as suffering from peripheral type carcinoma of the lung. His clinical diagnosis was primary cancer of the lower left bronchi of the lung.

6. Esophagitis

Esophagitis, in TCM, is categorized as diaphragmatic constriction. It is due to either a damaged spleen and bound qi, a damaged liver with depressed qi, or yin blood insufficiency. Individuals with this condition feel like they are choking no matter how little they eat. They also experience a bitter, cold, and frequent pain in the chest making it difficult to breath. The primary symptom of this disease is not difficulty in swallowing but the burning hot pain at their sternum. Other symptoms are heart sounds and sighing. This condition is mostly categorized as binding heat and diaphragmatic constriction.

Fingernail sign location: The central part of the index fingernail.

Fingernail sign shape: Strip, stick, or splay-like shapes

Fingernail sign color & luster: Light red between occurences; bright red during episodes

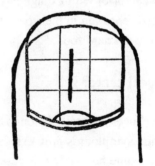

Esophagitis manifesting on the right index fingernail

Case 1: A 50-year-old female farmer came in on December 4, 1987, to have a nail check. A strip-shaped, longitudinal sign was seen on the central part of both her left and right index fingernails. The far extremity of the symbol was relatively thick with a cut mark, while the near extremity of the sign was bright red. Dr. Wang's diagnosis was esophagitis that was more severe in the lower part of the esophagus.

Upon being asked her medical history, the patient stated that she experienced swelling and pain at the back edge of her sternum with a burning hot, obstructed sensation when food was swallowed. Previously, she had been examined in different hospitals and was diagnosed by all as suffering from esophagitis that was more severe in the lower part of her esophagus.

Case 2: A 35-year-old male worker came in on October 5, 1987. A stick-shaped sign with a light red color was found on the central part of his right index fingernail. Therefore, Dr. Wang's nail diagnosis was chronic esophagitis. On October 9, this diagnosis was confirmed by endoscopic examination.

Case 3: A 25-year-old male bus driver came in on December 26, 1986, for a nail exam. There was a stick-shaped sign with a bright red color on the central part of his right index fingernail. Its far extremity had a round end with a purplish-red color. Dr. Wang's fingernail diagnosis was esophagitis that was presently occurring. The patient stated that he had had an endoscopy in the hospital 1 week prior with a diagnosis of acute esophagitis. His main symptom was a burning hot, distended sensation in the front of his chest. His symptoms worsened after eating, and he did not dare to eat hard food.

7. Esophageal cancer

Esophageal cancer generally belongs to the category of diaphragmatic constriction in TCM. The most common symptom is progressive difficulty in swallowing. If the lungs become damaged, the qi may become bound. In this case, fluids will not be transported and flow. Rather, they gather together to form phlegm. If the liver becomes damaged, the qi may become depressed, in which case, the blood cannot flow smoothly and gathers together to form stasis. This phlegm and stasis may then obstruct the diaphragm so that the upper and lower parts of the body cannot connect or circulate. Therefore, according to TCM theory, this disease has a close relationship with the lungs and liver.

Fingernail sign location: The central part of the index fingernail

Fingernail sign shape: A dot

Fingernail sign color & luster: Black, purplish-black, or light yellow

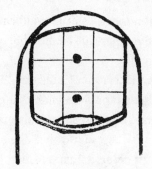

Esophageal cancer manifesting on the right index fingernail

Case: A 58-year-old male farmer came in on December 6, 1987. A dot-shaped symbol was found on both the far and near extremities of the central part of the right index fingernail. The color of the sign at the far extremity was purplish-black. At the near extremity, it was purplish red. A line-shaped sign connected these two dots. It was also a purplish red color. The same sign was also found on his left index fingernail; only the color was comparatively lighter. All of these symbols indicated that he had esophageal cancer.

After Dr. Wang's diagnosis, the patient stated that he had a blocked sensation when swallowing food and he had not been able to eat any hard food for over 3 months. It was suggested that the patient have a barium meal and x-ray examination of his esophagus in the hospital. This later positively diagnosed cancer of the upper section of the esophagus.

8. Coronary atherosclerotic heart disease

Coronary atherosclerotic heart disease, in TCM, is categorized as true heart pain and thoracic *bi*. If spleen yang does not transport and the life gate's fire becomes debilitated, heart yang may not rise. On the other hand, if the lungs and kidneys become yin vacuous and heart blood becomes insufficient, this may also cause heart yang not to rise. If heart yang does not rise, cold congeals to form blood stasis. If there is also phlegm turbidity internally, *bi* obstructs the heart vessels and qi and blood no longer circulate. This lack of circulation then causes pain and gripping heart pain occurs. If the condition is even more serious, this may result in myocardial infarction. Thus, in TCM, priority in terms of disease mechanisms involved in this disorder is given to heart yang not rising and blood stasis obstructing internally.

Fingernail sign location: The middle and far extremity of the ulnar side of the left middle fingernail

Fingernail sign shape: Most commonly, a triangular shape; oval shapes can also be seen.

Fingernail sign color & luster: Light red, purplish-red

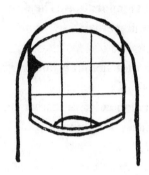

Coronary heart disease manifesting on the left middle fingernail

Case 1: A 60-year-old male retired worker came in on March 14, 1988. He stated that he had chest oppression and that it had been worse lately. He had no history of heart disease but also had had no tests. A nail check found a dark purple-colored, oval-shaped sign on the near extremity of the central part of the left middle fingernail. Dr. Wang's diagnosis was myocardial infarction. The patient was given an EKG examination, which showed an old, low wall, myocardial infarction.

Case 2: A 47-year-old female accountant was seen on June 24, 1987. Her complaint was chest oppression and shortness of breath over the last two years. Occasionally during the last year, she had had palpitations. A light red, triangular shaped sign was found on the central part of the ulnar side of her left middle fingernail. A purplish-red, strip-shaped sign was also seen on the central part of the same fingernail. Dr. Wang's diagnosis of this patient was coronary heart disease and sinus tachycardia. Her heart rate was 112 beats per minute. She was immediately given an EKG, which indicated myocardial ischemia.

9. Rheumatic heart disease

According to TCM, rheumatic heart disease may be categorized as racing of the heart, dyspnea condition, or water swelling, depending on its main presenting signs and symptoms. In this disease, wind, cold, and damp evils may invade the body causing internal damage and eventually reaching the heart. Thus the heart vessels become obstructed (*bi*) with pain and the

156

heart loses its nourishment. The lung qi becomes repressed and the qi becomes stagnant while the blood becomes static. This may extend to the triple burner and cause the spleen to lose its transforming and transporting function and the kidneys to no longer transform the qi. The triple burner then does not drain, and water intimidates the heart and lungs. Therefore, this disease's main symptoms are due to yang qi vacuity of the three viscera of the heart, spleen, and kidneys.

Fingernail sign location: The middle and far extremity of the ulnar side of the left middle fingernail

Fingernail sign shape: Strip or triangle

Fingernail sign color & luster: light red, purplish-red

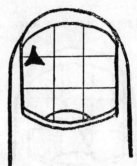

Rheumatic heart disease manifesting on the left middle fingernail

Case: A 43-year-old female came in on December 18, 1987 for a nail check. A triangular-shaped sign with a purplish-red color was observed on the middle and far extremity of the ulnar side of her left middle fingernail. Dr. Wang's diagnosis was rheumatic heart disease with the possibility of mitral stenosis. The patient stated that she had had rheumatic heart disease for over 10 years. She often felt nervous, had palpitations, and, at times, premature beats. It had been confirmed in the hospital the previous year by ultrasonic cardiography and X-ray that she had rheumatic heart disease and mitral stenosis.

10. Paroxysmal tachycardia

Paroxysmal tachycardia is called palpitation in TCM. It may come and go at no fixed intervals. Its symptoms may be due to either vacuity or repletion. For instance, paroxysmal tachycardia may be due to heart blood insufficiency, in which case yin cannot vanquish yang. It may also be due to constitutional yin vacuity with minute yin but exuberant yang. This results in the pulse beating extremely excessively and too often. Clinically, paroxysmal ventricular tachycardia and sinus tachycardia are the most commonly seen varieties of this condition, and the fingernail signs of these two are not exactly the same.

Fingernail sign location: The middle of the left middle fingernail

Fingernail sign shape: A long, longitudinal or slanted strip

Fingernail sign color & luster: Light red

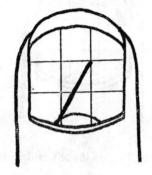

Paroxysmal tachycardia manifesting
on the left middle fingernail

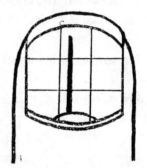

Paroxysmal ventricular tachycardia
manifesting on the left middle fingernail

Case 1: A 33-year-old female engineer came in on December 18, 1987, for a nail check. A long, strip-shaped sign slanting to the right with a light red color was observed at the center of her left middle fingernail. Dr. Wang diagnosed her as suffering from paroxysmal ventricular tachycardia. The patient stated that she had experienced palpitations and chest oppression for over 2 years. Initially, these occurred every 1-3 months. Later, both the frequency and length of their episodes increased. She also experienced fatigue and dizziness, and her heart rate sometimes reached 180-200 beats per minute. An EKG was performed and her diagnosis was, indeed, paroxysmal ventricular tachycardia.

Case 2: A 29-year-old female factory worker came in on March 17, 1987 because of nervousness and chest oppression. A nail check disclosed a long, longitudinal, strip-shaped sign with a purplish-red color going from the near extremity to the far extremity at the center of her left middle fingernail. The diagnosis was sinus tachycardia. Her heart rate was 136 beats per minute. An EKG revealed sinus tachycardia.

11. Premature beat

Premature beat, also called extra systole and premature systole, is referred to as a skipping pulse, bound pulse, or regularly interrupted pulse in TCM. In clinical practice, there is a difference between a functional and pathological premature beat. The main symptom is that the heartbeat pauses or increases suddenly. An incidental premature beat usually has no conscious symptom. In TCM, this condition is related to damage of the qi and blood, qi stagnation and blood stasis, or *bi* obstruction of the network vessels of the heart.

Fingernail sign location: The near and far extremities of the center of the left middle fingernail and the near and far extremities of the central part of the left index fingernail (the last rarely seen)

Fingernail sign shape: A dot

Fingernail sign color & luster: Light red

Premature beat manifesting on the left middle fingernail

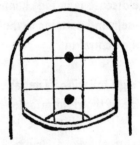

Premature beat manifesting on the left index fingernail

Case 1: A 57-year-old male came in on March 17, 1987, due to chest oppression and rapid breathing. When Dr. Wang examined his fingernails, a round, light red, dot-shaped sign was found on both the near and far extremities of the central part of his left middle fingernail. Dr. Wang's diagnosis of this patient was premature beat. After the nail exam, the patient stated that he had felt like his heart had stopped beating constantly for over a year. A total of 8 EKG exams had been done. Only one of these had diagnosed premature ventricular beat.

Case 2: A 62-year-old female retired factory worker came in on December 6, 1987. On nail exam, a purplish-red, round, dot-shaped sign was found on both the near and far extremities of the center of her left middle fingernail. A purplish-red, thin line linked these two dots. Her diagnoses were premature beat and sinus tachycardia. One month previously, the patient had had an EKG exam that had diagnosed premature ventricular beat and sinus tachycardia.

Middle Burner Diseases

1. Chronic gastritis

In TCM, chronic gastritis is categorized as stomach venter pain, liver/stomach qi pain, and stomach reflux. Clinical symptoms vary from patient to patient but include poor assimilation, gastric discomfort, belching, and nausea. The causes according to TCM theory are the liver losing its coursing and draining, the stomach losing its harmony and downbearing, and the liver and stomach being disharmonious. In that case, there is depressed heat in the liver and stomach. Initially, the disease is in the channels and pertains to the qi. In enduring disease, it enters the network vessels and pertains to the blood. Long-term pain without an effective cure can lead to damage of the central qi.

Fingernail sign location: The far extremity of the radial side of the right middle fingernail

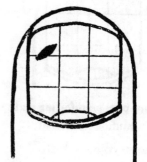

Fingernail sign shape: A strip or oval

Fingernail sign color & luster: Light red between episodes; purplish-red during occurrences

Chronic gastritis manifesting on the right middle fingernail

Case 1: A 42-year-old woman came in on March 2, 1987, for a nail exam. A purplish-red, oval-shaped sign on the far extremity of the radial side of her right middle fingernail was found. Her diagnosis was chronic gastritis, presently occurring. The patient stated that she had experienced stomach bloating, belching, and loss of appetite. She later had an endoscopic examination on March 4 and was diagnosed with atrophic gastritis.

Case 2: A 10-year-old female student came in on September 28, 1986 for a nail exam. A purplish-red, strip-shaped sign slanting from the lower left to the upper right was seen on the center and far extremity of the radial side of her right middle fingernail. The area around this sign appeared light red. Her nail diagnosis was chronic gastritis primarily affecting the gastric antrum. This diagnosis was confirmed by barium meal and X-ray exam. The patient was given herbal treatment.

2. Duodenal ulcer

In TCM, duodenal ulcers belong to the category of stomach venter pain, liver/stomach qi pain, and heart pain. Their main symptoms are periodic, rhythmic pain in the gastric cavity, belching, and acid regurgitation. The cause is usually depressed qi damaging the liver. The liver qi, therefore, counterflows horizontally and the spleen and stomach are checked. The qi mechanism is obstructed and stagnant and accumulation over time turns into disease. As this disease condition worsens, depressed qi transforms into fire and the stomach vessels are damaged, thus causing bleeding.

Fingernail sign location: The far extremity of the center of the right middle fingernail

Fingernail sign shape: Round, oval, or triangular

Fingernail sign color & luster: Light red between episodes; bright red or purplish-red during occurrences

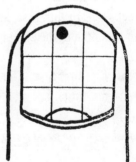

Duodenal ulcer manifesting on the right middle fingernail

Case 1: A 44-year-old male engineer was seen on December 11, 1987. A purplish-red colored, triangular-shaped symbol was seen on the far extremity of the center of his right middle fingernail. Dr. Wang diagnosed this patient as suffering from duodenal ulcer. Upper abdominal discomfort was the patient's only obvious symptom. A few days later, a barium meal and X-ray exam confirmed Dr. Wang's fingernail diagnosis.

Case 2: A 55-year-old male factory worker came in on December 17, 1987 due to palpitations and shortness of breath. During the nail exam, the patient also mentioned feeling distention and pain in his upper abdominal area. The pain was insidious. A long, oval-shaped sign was observed on his right middle fingernail from the center and far extremity of the radial side slanting toward the far extremity of the central part. The two ends of this sign showed a dark purplish color and the center part appeared purplish-red. His diagnosis was antral gastritis and duodenal ulcer. The patient then revealed a written gastroscopic report with his diagnosis of chronic atrophic gastritis and duodenal bulbar ulcer with deformity and frostlike spots.

3. Stomach cancer

In TCM, stomach cancer belongs to the category of diaphragmatic constriction and stomach reflux. It is caused by qi stagnation, blood stasis, and phlegm congelation. In its early stage, there are no obvious symptoms and it is often misdiagnosed as indigestion. If the stasis binds for a long period of time, then the lateral coastal region becomes bitter (*i.e.*, painful) and full. The stomach is not able to receive and absorb food, the network vessels are damaged, and thus blood seeps out. In this case, any vomitus appears like red bean juice. This disease is related to the qi and blood and the spleen and stomach.

Fingernail sign location: The center of radial side of right middle fingernail

Fingernail sign shape: Triangular, oval, or mist-like

Fingernail sign color & luster: Dark black, purplish-red

Stomach cancer manifesting on the right middle fingernail

Case: A 33-year-female old factory worker came in on April 1, 1988, for a nail exam. A dark, black colored, triangular shaped sign was observed on the center of the radial side of her right middle fingernail. Below this, a purplish-red colored, oval-shaped sign was also observed. These two symbols were connected by a white, strip-shaped sign. These signs indicated a previous surgery for stomach cancer, mainly in the area of the gastric antrum.

The patient disclosed her previous history of surgery for carcinoma of the stomach. The diagnosis pre-surgery had been gastric antrum ulcer. Post-surgical pathology reports and surgical observation diagnosed carcinoma of the back wall of the gastric antrum, ulceration of the back wall of the stomach, and inflammation of the lesser curvature of the stomach. The patient still felt distension and belched 4 months after the surgery.

4. Chronic hepatitis

In TCM, chronic hepatitis belongs to the categories of lateral costal region pain and jaundice. It is usually due to chronic infection by a hepatitis virus that has not been able to be cured. Its main symptoms are fullness in the chest, aversion to food, spirit fatigue, lack of strength, abdominal distention, and lateral costal region pain. The cause is dampness and turbidity obstructing internally. In TCM, this disease is divided into two main types: vacuity and repletion. In the vacuity type, the righteous qi is vacuous. This is usually due to spleen vacuity. In the repletion type, evil repletion is usually due to exuberant dampness. The early stage is typically due to repletion, while the later stage is typically due to vacuity. This disease is very closely related to the liver, gallbladder, spleen, and stomach.

Fingernail sign location: The near extremity of the center part of the right ring fingernail and the center part of the ulnar side of the right ring fingernail

Fingernail sign shape: Round, triangular, or mist-like

Fingernail sign color & luster: Light red or purplish-red

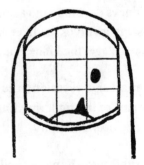

Chronic hepatitis manifesting on the right ring fingernail

Case: A 34-year-old male factory worker came in on February 24, 1987, for a nail exam. A purplish-red, oval-shaped sign was observed on the center and near extremities of the ulnar side of his right ring fingernail. Around it was a light red, misty-shaped sign. Within the oval-shaped sign, a white strip was also observed. A purplish-red, triangular-shaped sign was also seen on the near extremity of the center of the same fingernail. Dr. Wang's diagnosis of this patient was chronic hepatitis with the possibility of elevated transaminase levels and hepatomegaly.

The patient was requested to have an ultrasound and serological liver function tests. The patient previously had had hepatitis in 1983 and ultrasound had revealed hepatomegaly in 1986. He had recently felt lateral costal region pain, fatigue, abdominal distention, reduced appetite, and, on occasion, nausea. On March 2, 1987, the patient returned with a test report showing SGPT (serum glutamic-pyruvic transaminase) at 60 units, TTT (thymol turbidity test) at 14 units, and hepatitis B surface antigen positive. He requested herbal treatment.

5. Cirrhosis of the liver

In TCM, early stage cirrhosis is called lateral costal region pain, while in the advanced stage it is called drum distension. In this disease, the main pathological changes occurring in the liver are chronic and progressive ones. Due to enduring liver disease, the liver becomes depressed and this damages the spleen. Thus, both the liver and spleen become diseased. Qi stagnates and blood becomes static. This then affects kidney yin to its detriment. Eventually both the liver and kidneys develop yin vacuity and the condition's nature becomes malignant. In sum, the early stage involves the liver and spleen, while, in the advanced stage, the kidneys are also involved.

Fingernail sign location: The near extremity of the center part of the right ring fingernail or the ulnar side near extremity

Fingernail sign shape: Round or triangular

Fingernail sign color & luster: Purplish-red, purplish-black

Cirrhosis of the liver manifesting on the right ring fingernail

Case 1: A 49-year-old male factory worker came in on April 1, 1988, for a nail exam. A round-shaped sign with a black dot was seen on both the near extremity of the center of the right ring fingernail and the near extremity of the ulnar side of the right ring fingernail. This indicated cirrhosis of the liver. The patient stated that he had a history of hepatitis and that his serum transaminase levels had increased in 1979. However, this had been cured. Since the patient also complained of poor assimilation, emaciation, fatigue, abdominal distention and discomfort, and occasional bleeding gums, an ultrasound exam was performed. By this exam, he was diagnosed with cirrhosis of the liver, splenomegaly, and ascites. The clinical diagnosis was cirrhosis of the liver and portal hypertension.

Case 2: A 64-year-old male came in on April 2, 1988, for a nail exam. A dark purple-colored, triangular-shaped sign was found on the near extremity of the center of his right ring fingernail. His diagnosis was cirrhosis of the liver. The patient had no history of hepatitis. However, the year before he had received treatment at a hospital for abdominal distention and poor appetite. The medications he took at that time were of no help. On February 12, 1988, he was diagnosed by ultrasound with cirrhosis of the liver and splenomegaly.

6. Liver cancer

In TCM, liver cancer falls under the categories of jaundice, drum distention, and/or concretions, conglomerations, accumulations, and gatherings. Its disease causes and disease mechanisms are similar to cirrhosis of the liver. Initially, there is liver depression and qi stagnation. Long-term qi stagnation within the body forms blood stasis. Because of blood stasis and qi congestion, there is *bi* obstruction and no free flow. Hence bound lumps are formed in the body.

Fingernail sign location: The near extremity of the center part of the right ring fingernail

Fingernail sign shape: Round or oval

Fingernail sign color & luster: Black

Liver cancer manifesting on the right ring fingernail

Case: A 44-year-old male engineer came in on April 2, 1988 for a nail exam. A horizontal, oval-shaped sign was observed on the near extremity of the center of his right ring fingernail. The tip of the inner side of this sign had a black dot. The rest of the sign was a purplish-red color. All of these signs indicated cancer of the liver. The patient stated he had had hepatitis in 1979, cirrhosis of the liver in 1983, and ascites in 1986, but the ascites had vanished after treatment. During the last 3 months, a large amount of ascitic fluid had reappeared. His diagnosis by ultrasound was cancer of the liver. He looked very thin and had a faded, green facial color. His clinical diagnosis was cirrhosis of the liver, primary cancer of the liver, and portal hypertension.

7. Chronic cholecystitis

There is no traditional Chinese medical name for chronic cholecystitis. However, in the *Ling Shu (Spiritual Pivot)*, its symptoms are clearly recorded. Gallbladder distention with distention and pain in the lateral costal region and liver distention with fullness in the lateral costal region and pain radiating to the lower abdomen both refer to this condition. In TCM, it is believed that this disease is due to liver/gallbladder qi stagnation and damp heat congesting and obstructing. Thus the bile cannot be excreted uninhibitedly.

Fingernail sign location: The near extremity of the ulnar side of the right ring fingernail

Fingernail sign shape: A strip-like shape

Fingernail sign color & luster: Light red between flare-ups; bright red or purplish-red during occurrences

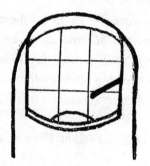

Chronic cholecystitis manifesting on the right ring fingernail

Case 1: A 49-year-old man came in on April 15, 1987. He complained of discomfort in the area of *Zhong Wan* (CV 12), oppression and distention, and insidious pain for nearly 2 years. These did not improve even after taking medicines for stomach pain. However, when Dr. Wang inspected this patient's fingernails, there was no sign for stomach pain on his right middle fingernail. But there was a slanting, strip-shaped sign with a light red color observed on the near extremity of the ulnar side of his right ring fingernail. According to Chinese fingernail diagnosis, there was no stomach problem. The discomfort this man felt at *Zhong Wan* was caused by cholecystitis. Five days later a diagnosis of chronic cholecystitis was confirmed by ultrasound in the hospital.

Case 2: A 46-year-old woman came in on December 6, 1986, because of distention and pain in her epigastric area and palpitations. On examining her fingernails, Dr. Wang observed a bright red, strip-shaped sign on the center and near extremities of the ulnar side of her right ring fingernail. A round, dot-shaped sign with a purplish-red color was also observed within this strip. Dr. Wang's diagnosis of this patient was cholecystitis with the possibility of gallstones. Two weeks later, ultrasound confirmed that she had cholecystitis and cholelithiasis.

8. Chronic pancreatitis

The pancreas is not named as one of the five viscera or six bowels of Traditional Chinese Medicine. However, in TCM, the functions of the pancreas are related to both the liver and the spleen. Traditional Chinese disease categories related to diseases of the pancreas are spleen/heart pain, liver/stomach disharmony, and chest bind. Due to abnormal function of the liver, gallbladder, spleen, and stomach, the qi mechanism may lose its ability of upbearing and downbearing. Qi then stagnates, congests, obstructs, and congeals into stasis. Depression transforms wind (*i.e.*, liver qi) into heat, and damp heat obstructs the middle burner.

Fingernail sign location: The middle and near extremities of the center of the ring fingernail or the middle and near extremities of the radial side of the left middle fingernail

Fingernail sign shape: Triangular, cone, or strip shapes

Fingernail sign color & luster: Light red between episodes; bright red or purplish-red during flare-ups

Chronic pancreatitis manifesting on the right ring fingernail

Chronic pancreatitis manifesting on the left ring fingernail

Case: A 36-year-old female farmer was seen on December 24, 1986. A purplish-red, cone-shaped sign was observed on both the near extremity of the center of her left ring fingernail and the near extremity of the radial side of her left middle fingernail. The middle section of the center of her right ring fingernail also had a straight, strip-shaped sign with a purplish-red color. All of these indicated pancreatitis. The patient then stated that she had frequently experienced pain in her upper abdominal area, nausea, discomfort, and bloating after meals for almost 2 years. Six month ago, she had had an ultrasound examination that confirmed chronic pancreatitis. Due to a lack of marked results from prior treatment, she was seeking treatment with Chinese herbal medicine.

9. Hepatomegaly & splenomegaly

Hepatomegaly and splenomegaly share similar signs. In TCM, the different causes of hepatomegaly and splenomegaly all belong to the category of concretions, conglomerations, accumulations, and gatherings. If the liver and spleen are damaged, the viscera and bowels lose their harmony and qi may counterflow, while blood becomes static. After a period of time, stagnation becomes accumulation. Liver accumulation, one of the so-called five accumulations, is called fat qi. It is located under the left lateral costal region and in shape appears like a cup.

Splenomegaly is similar. The spleen accumulation is called glomus qi. It is located in the epigastrium and in shape is like a large plate. If this is not cured, after a long time, it will make the four limbs unable to contact and jaundice will appear. Hepatomegaly and splenomegaly indicate pathological changes that should be further observed and tested in order to confirm their diagnosis.

Fingernail sign location: The location of hepatomegaly and splenomegaly signs are different. The first is located on the near extremity of the center of the right ring fingernail. The second is located on the near extremity of the center of the left ring fingernail. Some signs lean toward the near extremity of the ulnar side. Some splenomegaly signs lean toward the near extremity of the radial side.

Fingernail sign shape: Cone or triangular

Fingernail sign color & luster: Light red or purplish-red

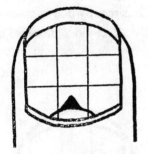

Hepatomegaly manifesting on the right ring fingernail

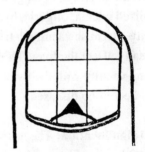

Splenomegaly manifesting on the left ring fingernail

Case 1: A 52-year-old female retiree came in on February 28, 1987, due to fullness of the chest and distention in the area of *Zhong Wan* (CV 12). A purple-colored, cone-shaped sign was observed on the near extremity of the center of her right ring fingernail. The patient was told she had hepatomegaly and needed an ultrasound examination. On March 7, she sent a letter stating that the ultrasound had confirmed that she did have hepatomegaly.

Case 2: A 34-year-old male technician came in on November 27, 1986, for a nail exam. A light red, triangular-shaped sign was observed on the near extremity of the center of his left ring fingernail. His diagnosis was splenomegaly. One week later, ultrasound confirmed the diagnosis of splenomegaly.

Case 3: A 34-year-old man came in on November 2, 1987, for a nail exam. A light red, cone-shaped sign was observed at both the near extremity of the center of his left and right ring fingernails. His fingernail diagnosis was, therefore, both hepatomegaly and splenomegaly. The patient then stated that he already had had an ultrasound that confirmed both the hepatomegaly and the splenomegaly.

Lower Burner Diseases

1. Chronic nephritis

In TCM, chronic nephritis belongs to the category of water swelling disease. Its main symptoms are generalized edema, oliguria, hematuria, and hypertension. It is mainly due to spleen/kidney yang vacuity. Because vacuity detriment to yang will eventually affect yin, a diseased kidney will eventually affect the liver. This then results in both yin and yang vacuity with the liver, spleen, and kidneys all becoming diseased.

Fingernail sign location: The near extremity of the ulnar side of the ring fingernail

Fingernail sign shape: Triangular, crescent, or mist-like

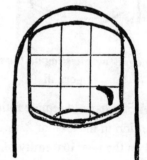

Fingernail sign color & luster: Light red or purplish-red

Chronic nephritis manifesting on the right ring fingernail

Case 1: A 40-year-old female farmer came in on December 19, 1987. She complained of low back pain and facial edema for over 6 months. When Dr. Wang examined her fingernails, a bright red, triangular-shaped sign was observed on the near extremity of the ulnar side of her right ring fingernail. This indicated nephritis. She left a urine sample for laboratory testing. The test results showed proteinuria, red blood cells in her urine, and granular casts. The patient had been unaware of her chronic nephritis before this.

Case 2: A 41-year-old female factory worker came in for a nail exam. A purplish-red, crescent-shaped sign was observed on the near extremity of the ulnar side of both her right and left ring fingernails. The patient then stated she had had chronic nephritis for 11 years and that the hospital was already treating her.

2. Chronic colitis

In TCM, chronic colitis is categorized as either dysentery disease, intestinal wind, visceral toxins, or diarrhea. Its main signs are diarrhea and abdominal pain. It is most often caused by damp heat that brews and binds in the large intestine. After a period of time, this damages the spleen and stomach. It may also be due to liver qi depression and binding. This results in horizontal counterflow invading the stomach and damaging the spleen. In this case, spleen yang is not fortified and spleen qi becomes insufficient. Thus this disease occurs.

Fingernail sign location: The near extremity of the radial side of the right middle fingernail

Fingernail sign shape: A strip, semi-circular shape, or a mist-like shape

Fingernail sign color & luster: Light red or bright red

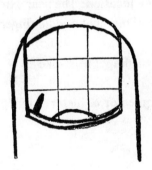

Chronic colitis manifesting on the right middle fingernail

Case: A 55-year-old woman came in on November 11, 1987, for a nail exam. She had been unable to work for over 1 year due to interrupted alimentary canal bleeding. The etiology of her disease was unclear. Other symptoms were insidious abdominal pain, frequent bowel movements, and occult blood in her stool. There was no mucus in her stool nor did she have any history of dysentery, food allergies, or swollen lumps. Her tongue coating was thin, yellow, and slimy. Her pulse was deep and fine. Testing by barium enema and X-ray was inconclusive. On her nails, however, there was a bright red, strip-shaped sign on the near extremity of the radial side of her right middle fingernail. Her diagnosis was, therefore, mild colitis, probably affecting the ascending colon. On November 25, test results by fiber optic colonoscopy confirmed Dr. Wang's fingernail diagnosis.

3. Constipation

In constipation, the stool is extremely dry and hard and is difficult to discharge. There are two main types of constipation in TCM: replete and vacuous. The replete type may be divided into two further types: dry heat, also called spleen constraint, and qi stagnation. In reference to the latter, it is said that, Qi stagnates internally and objects cannot move. Vacuity constipation may be differentiated into qi vacuity, blood vacuity, fluid and humor insufficiency, and vacuity cold constipation. Therefore, this disease is related not only to the viscera and bowels but also to the qi, blood, fluids, and humors.

Fingernail sign location: The near extremity of the radial side of the right middle fingernail

Fingernail sign shape: Mist-like

Fingernail sign color & luster: Light gray

Constipation manifesting on the right middle fingernail

Case: A 32-year-old male factory worker came in on March 25, 1987. On examination of his fingernails, a light gray, mist-like sign was observed on the near extremity of the radial side of his right middle fingernail. The diagnosis of habitual constipation was then verbally confirmed by the patient. He only had 1-2 bowel movements per week and these were very dry. He often used laxatives.

4. Chronic prostatitis

In TCM, chronic prostatitis belongs to the categories of essence turbidity and taxation strangury. Its signs are mostly related to kidney vacuity. When white turbidity seeps out of the urinary tract, this is due to turbidity in the essence combining with fire. Fire causes frenetic movement or counterflow, which, in turn, causes the essence to flow out with the urine. Because the source of turbidity is the spleen, this disease is related to kidney qi vacuity, abnormal transformation function of the spleen and stomach, and damp heat congestion and obstruction as well as qi stagnation and blood stasis.

Fingernail sign location: The far and near extremities of the left ring fingernail

Fingernail sign shape: Dumb-bell or strip-shaped

Fingernail sign color & luster: Light red or purplish-red

Chronic prostatitis manifesting on the left ring fingernail

Case: A 66-year-old man came in on January 8, 1988, for a nail exam. A vertical, slightly slanting, dumb-bell shaped sign with a purplish-red color was observed on the center of his left ring fingernail. Dr. Wang, therefore, told the patient that he had chronic prostatitis. The patient later had a digital rectal exam and laboratory tests in the hospital. These confirmed that he did have chronic prostatitis.

5. Prostatic hypertrophy

In TCM, prostatic hypertrophy is called dribbling urinary block. Its main symptoms clinically are urinary frequency, urinary block, urinary incontinence, and dysuria. It is caused by lung qi not diffusing, spleen qi vacuity weakness, kidney yin insufficiency, kidney yang weakness and debility, central qi falling, damp heat sinking, and stasis obstructing the bladder. Because its causation involves viscera located in all three burners, in TCM it is said to be related to the triple burner. The triple burner is the official of the sluices in charge of the water passageways.

Fingernail sign location: The far and near
extremities of the center of the ring fingernail

Fingernail sign shape: Triangular

Fingernail sign color & luster: Light red

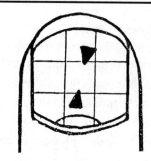

Prostatic hypertrophy manifesting on the left ring fingernail

Case: A 46-year-old man came in on October 6, 1987, for a nail exam. A light red, triangular-shaped sign was observed on both the far and near extremities of the center line of his left ring fingernail. This indicated prostatic hyperplasia. The patient then confirmed that he had been diagnosed with this condition earlier in April of that year. His main symptom at that time was dysuria.

6. Uterine fibroids

In TCM, uterine fibroids are classified as concretions and gatherings. They are due to lumps binding in the uterus. This is a repletion pattern. It is caused by viscera and bowel disharmony, in which case the qi mechanism becomes obstructed and stagnates. This leads to blood stasis becoming lodged and stagnant, gradually accumulating and causing concretions. After some time, qi and blood become greatly debilitated and this can cause concomitant yang vacuity. Clinically, uterine fibroids are differentiated into blood stasis type and qi and blood vacuity type.

Fingernail sign location: The near extremity
of the radial side of the ring fingernail

Fingernail sign shape: Oval, crescent, or strip-shaped

Fingernail sign color & luster: Light red or purplish-red

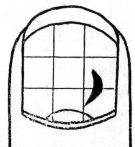

Uterine fibroids manifesting on the left ring fingernail

Case: A 43-year-old female factory worker came in on October 28, 1987, for a nail exam. Her symptoms were chest oppression and palpitations. A crescent-shaped sign with a purplish-red color was observed on the center and near extremity of the radial side of her left ring fingernail. This indicated the possibility of uterine fibroids. The patient reported symptoms of increased menstrual blood flow, abdominal distention, and low back pain. She then showed her latest ultrasound report confirming Dr. Wang's diagnosis.

7. Salpingitis

In TCM, salpingitis, which is included in pelvic inflammation, is categorized under abnormal vaginal discharge and/or female concretions and gatherings. Acute salpingitis is caused by heat toxins, damp turbidity, and evil qi congesting and becoming exuberant. It is a repletion pattern. Chronic salpingitis is usually caused by coldness congealing, qi stagnating, and damp heat depression and binding. If the fallopian tube becomes obstructed and, on palpation, a cord-like object can be felt, this is categorized as a vacuity pattern due to spleen/kidney insufficiency or a mixed pattern of vacuity and repletion.

Because salpingitis may easily affect the uterine adnexa, causing adnexitis, or the ovary, resulting in ovaritis, it is difficult to differentiate these precisely by Chinese fingernail diagnosis.

Fingernail sign location: The near extremity of the radial side of the ring fingernail

Fingernail sign shape: Mist-like

Fingernail sign color & luster: Light red between episodes and brighter during a flare-up

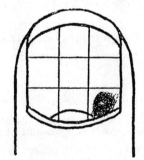

Salpingitis manifesting on the left ring fingernail

Case: A 40-year-old female engineer came in on August 24, 1987, for a nail exam. An oval, mist-like sign with a light red color was observed on the near extremity of the radial side of her right ring fingernail. Dr. Wang's diagnosis of this patient was salpingitis. The patient confirmed that this was the diagnosis given her by the hospital some time previously. This disease condition had come and gone over the last 10 years.

Diseases of the Four Limbs and Joints

1. Rheumatoid arthritis

In TCM, rheumatoid arthritis is categorized as a *bi* pattern. Its main symptoms are heaviness, soreness, numbness, swelling, and pain of the joints and muscles. Patients with this condition thus find it difficult to stretch or contract their joints and muscles. This disease is caused by invasion of the three qi—wind, cold, and dampness—taking advantage of vacuity. When wind qi is dominant, this is called moving *bi*. When cold qi is dominant, this is called painful *bi*. When damp qi is dominant, this is called fixed *bi*. Because the liver rules the sinews and the kidneys govern the bones, if this disease lasts a long time, it will cause detriment and depletion to the liver and kidneys.

Fingernail sign location: The far extremity of the ring fingernail

Fingernail sign shape: A strip, dot, or both

Fingernail sign color & luster: Light red between episodes; bright red or purplish-red during flare-ups

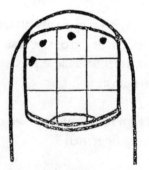

Rheumatoid arthritis manifesting on the ring fingernail

Case 1: A 43-year-old woman came in on August 21, 1987. Three oval-shaped signs with a purplish-red color were observed on the far extremity of both her right and left ring fingernails. Her diagnosis was rheumatoid arthritis severely affecting her knee joints. The patient stated she had gone to the hospital twice, in November of the previous year and in February of the present year. Tests showed a fast blood sedimentation rate and both knee joints were red and swollen. It was difficult for her to walk. Her hospital diagnosis had been rheumatoid arthritis.

Case 2: A 28-year-old male factory worker came in on September 28, 1986, for a nail exam. Three signs were seen at the far extremity of both his right and left ring fingernails. In the center was a light red, round-shaped sign. The two at the sides were slanted, strip-shaped signs. One was a light red and the other was a purplish-red color. Dr. Wang's fingernail diagnosis of this patient was rheumatoid arthritis. The patient stated he had had arthritis for 4 years. When the arthritis occurred, both knees were painful. He had even purchased protective knee pads.

2. Periarthritis of the shoulder

In TCM, periarthritis of the shoulder is called leaking shoulder wind, frozen bound shoulder, congealed shoulder, or fifty year shoulder. All these belong to the category of *bi zheng*. Its TCM causes are taxation detriment with contraction of wind and dampness. Evil qi thus blocks and obstructs the sinews and bones. The sinew vessels become tense and there is fixed pain. It is difficult for the joints to stretch. If the disease detriment lasts for a prolonged period of time, the constructive and defensive may become empty and vacuous with a tendency toward bone *bi*.

Fingernail sign location: The far extremity of the radial side or ulnar side of the index fingernail

Fingernail sign shape: A round dot

Fingernail sign color & luster: Light red, bright red, or purplish-red

Periarthritis of the shoulder manifesting on the right index fingernail

Case 1: A 49-year-old woman came in for a nail exam on September 28, 1986. A dot-shaped sign was observed on the far extremity of the radial side of both her right and left index fingernails. The sign on the left index fingernail was a bright red color. The sign on the right was a purplish red color. Dr. Wang's fingernail diagnosis of this patient was periarthritis of the shoulder, with the right side more severe than the left. The patient agreed with this diagnosis, stating that she had experienced pain for over 4 months and mainly on her right side. She could not lift this shoulder and she had pain if she moved it. Her family had to help her get dressed.

Case 2: A 29-year-old woman came in on February 24, 1987, for a nail exam. A round, dot-shaped sign with a bright red color was observed on the far extremity of the radial side of her right index fingernail. Her nail diagnosis was periarthritis of the shoulder. The patient stated that she had had difficulty moving that shoulder joint for the past 3 days. She noticed this when raising her hand at work and she could not externally rotate her shoulder. When she moved her shoulder, it was painful. The patient was currently receiving acupuncture for this condition.

3. Vertebral hypertrophy of the cervical, thoracic, & lumbar regions

In TCM, hypertrophy of the cervical, thoracic, and lumbar vertebrae also is categorized as *bi zheng*. It is due to the qi and blood of the channels and network vessels being blocked and obstructed by wind, cold, and damp environmental excess evils. Lumbodorsal and sacroiliac pain are all called lumbago or low back pain. The bones feel too heavy to lift and pain radiates from the buttocks to the heel and from the back to the head. Brachial neuralgia and ischialgia symptoms appear along their nerve paths and distribution areas.

In TCM, wind causes moving *bi*, cold causes painful *bi*, and damp causes fixed *bi*. Because the symptoms manifest in the joints of the four limbs, the lower and upper back, the channels and network vessels, and the blood vessels, in TCM this condition is diagnosed according to the channels on which these symptoms appear and from there to the viscera and bowels with which these channels are connected.

A. Cervical vertebral hypertrophy

Fingernail sign location: The far extremity of the ulnar side of the index fingernail

Fingernail sign shape: A strip-like shape

Fingernail sign color & luster: Light red or purplish-red

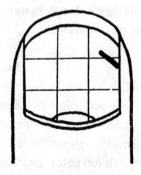

Hypertrophy of the cervical vertebrae manifesting on the right index fingernail

Case 1: A 22-year-old male student came in on September 18, 1986, for a nail exam. A strip-shaped sign was observed on the far extremity of the ulnar side of both his right and left index fingernails. The sign on the right index fingernail had a purplish red color and the sign on the left had a light red color. His diagnosis was hypertrophy of the cervical vertebrae.

This was a surprising diagnosis due to the young age of the patient. Nonetheless, the student and his family concurred with this diagnosis. The patient's neck was very stiff and painful. It was difficult for him to move his neck and, when he did so, it caused pain to radiate to his right shoulder and back. He also experienced numbness in his right hand and had unbearable pain. The condition had developed in 1984, causing pain in both shoulders. He had had X-rays of his neck in two hospitals, both confirming hypertrophy of C4 and C5 with pyramidal overgrowth.

Case 2: A 39-year-old male factory worker came in on November 17, 1986 for a nail exam. A slanting, strip-shaped sign with a light red color was observed on the far extremity of the ulnar side of his right index fingernail. His diagnosis was pyramidal overgrowth. The patient stated that his neck often felt stiff and distended. One month previously, X-rays had been taken confirming that he did have pyramidal overgrowth.

B. Thoracic vertebral hypertrophy

Fingernail sign location: The far extremity of the ulnar side of the right middle fingernail

Fingernail sign shape: Triangular, oval, or strip-shaped

Fingernail sign color & luster: Light red or purplish-red

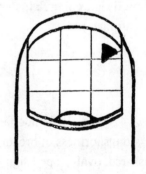

Hypertrophy of the thoracic vertebrae manifesting on the right middle fingernail

Case 1: A 46-year-old female factory worker came in on November 9, 1987, for a nail exam. A light red, oval-shaped sign was observed on the far extremity of the ulnar side of her right middle fingernail. Her nail diagnosis was hypertrophy of the thoracic vertebrae. The patient did not know that she had this condition. She did, however, experience stiffness and heaviness in the area of her upper and low back. It was suggested that she have X-rays taken. The patient returned on November 24 stating that the X-rays had showed vertebral overgrowth from T3-T7.

Case 2: A 40-year-old man came in on November 5, 1986, for a nail exam. A light red, triangular-shaped sign was observed on the far extremity of the ulnar side of his right middle fingernail. His fingernail diagnosis was hypertrophy of the thoracic vertebrae. The patient stated that X-rays of his thoracic vertebrae had been taken the previous month. They confirmed vertebral overgrowth at T6 and T7.

C. Lumbar vertebral hypertrophy

Fingernail sign location: The far extremity of the ulnar side of the ring fingernail

Fingernail sign shape: Oval, strip

Fingernail sign color & luster: Light red, bright red, or purplish-red

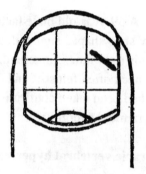

Hypertrophy of the lumbar vertebrae manifesting on the right ring fingernail

Case: A 42-year-old female factory worker came in on December 12, 1987, because of chest oppression, shortness of breath, and lumbar pain. Besides the sign for cervical hypertrophy, a purplish-red, oval-shaped sign was observed on the far extremity of the ulnar side of both her ring fingernails. Her fingernail diagnosis was lumbar vertebral hypertrophy. It was suggested that she have further X-rays taken. She had these on December 29 and the result was the diagnosis of cervical pyramidal hypertrophy at C6 and C7 and lumbar pyramidal hypertrophy at L2 and L4.

Other Diseases

1. Hypertension

In TCM, hypertension may be categorized under dizziness, headache, liver yang, or liver wind. Its main symptom is hypertension caused by an imbalance of yin and yang, namely of the liver and kidneys. Therefore, hypertension is related to the liver and kidney channels. In addition, the *chong mai* governs the blood and the *ren mai* rules the qi. When the *chong* and *ren* are imbalanced (in particular in women and commonly at menopause), they may cause liver yang hyperactivity. Thus, hypertension is also closely related to the *chong* and *ren*.

Fingernail sign location: The central part of the left index fingernail

Fingernail sign shape: A strip or dumb-bell shape

Fingernail sign color & luster: Light red

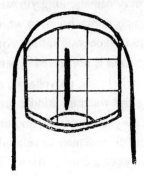

Hypertension manifesting on the left index fingernail

Case 1: A 74-year-old male came in on March 2, 1987, for a nail exam. A relatively thick, strip-shaped sign was observed on his left index fingernail. The sign went from the near extremity to the far extremity, vertically running through the center. His diagnosis was hypertension. The patient stated he had had hypertension for over 30 years. He had tried different types of treatment in the last 3-4 years trying to lower his blood pressure to normal. The hospital diagnosed his condition as third degree hypertension. His blood pressure tested at 190/118.

Case 2: A 65-year-old man came in on November 4, 1987, for a nail exam. His complaints were chest oppression, palpitations, and dizziness. On examining his fingernails, a straight, vertical, strip-shaped sign with a light red color was observed on the center of his left index fingernail. Another slanting strip-shaped sign with a light red color was observed on the radial side. His diagnosis was episodic hypertension. The patient confirmed this had been happening over the last 2 years. At its highest point, the systolic reading could reach over 200. At its low point, the systolic reading was around 90. His blood pressure was tested and was found to be 190/110. He returned a second time on November 29, 1987, and his blood pressure was 94/64.

2. Diabetes

In TCM, diabetes is referred to as wasting thirst. Its main symptoms are polydipsia, polyphagia, and polyuria with sugar in the urine. Yin vacuity and dry heat are the main causes of this disease. Heat may damage lung yin and dry the fluids. Therefore there is excessive drinking. Heat may damage stomach yin, in which case, stomach fire may become very exuberant. Therefore there is excessive eating. And heat may damage kidney yin. In that case, essence becomes scanty and is not stored. Therefore there is excessive urination. Because patients may display either polydipsia, polyphagia, and/or polyuria, this condition is further divided into upper thirsting and wasting, middle thirsting and wasting, lower thirsting and wasting, middle and lower thirsting and wasting, and upper, middle, and lower thirsting and wasting. Hence, in individuals, this disease may be related to the lungs, spleen, or kidneys or a combination thereof.

Fingernail sign location: The near extremity of the radial side of the left middle fingernail

Fingernail sign shape: A round dot

Fingernail sign color & luster: White

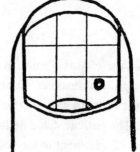

Diabetes manifesting on the left middle fingernail

Case 1: A 50-year-old woman came in on December 15, 1987, for a nail exam. A white, round, dot-shaped sign was observed on the near extremity of the radial side of her left middle fingernail. Dr. Wang stated that this sign indicated diabetes. The patient stated she had had diabetes for over 7 years. Her last hospital urine test was double plus positive for glucose and her blood glucose concentration was 178mg/100ml.

Case 2: A 45-year-old man came in on December 15, 1985, for a nail exam. A white, round, dot-shaped sign was observed on the near extremity of the radial side of his left middle fingernail. His fingernail diagnosis was diabetes. The patient was unaware that he had this condition. He did report a good appetite and frequent urination. Afterwards, a glucose tolerance test confirmed the diagnosis of diabetes.

Appendix I
Palm Prints

Palm prints are a useful aid in practicing Chinese medical palmistry. Although one does not have to take palm prints of each person whose palm they look at, professional health care practitioners should consider taking patients' palm prints for two reasons. First, if one has the patient's palm print on file, one can study it at length even when the patient is no longer present. Thus one can look at it under magnification and while researching texts on palmistry such as this. Secondly, such prints can be included as part of each patient's permanent file. Prints taken at different points in time can then reveal any changes in the patient's condition.

In order to make a palm print, the practitioner will need some ink and a roller purchased from an art supply store, a thick piece of glass with polished edges, some white paper, a pencil, a fixative spray, also available from an art supply store, and some water, soap, and towels to clean up.

One first pours some ink on the glass and then, using the roller, one spreads this out very thinly and evenly across the glass. One then presses the palm down onto this ink and from there onto a piece of flat paper. While the hand is resting firmly on the paper without moving, the practitioner should carefully trace around the hand and fingers with a pencil to record the outer shape of the hand.

When the patient removes their hand, the practitioner should inspect the print carefully to make sure there are no smudges or blurs and that all the lines and fingerprints are clearly visible. If not, the process should be repeated one or more times until a good set of prints is obtained.

After both hands are done, the patient may then clean their hands with soap and water. After the prints have dried, the practitioner should spray a thin coating of fixative over the prints to prevent smudging. After this fixative spray has dried, one then has a permanent record, including the fingerprints discussed in Chapter 3 of Book One. These prints may be inserted

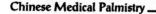

into clear plastic sleeves in order to keep them clean and unwrinkled. If the practitioner is a professional health care provider, these can be stored along with the rest of the patient's file.

Appendix II
Eight Trigram Palmistry

Eight trigram Chinese palmistry is an indigenous Chinese system of palmistry associated with folk-Daoism and Chinese shamans. Some authorities on Chinese palmistry feel that this system was not originally based on actual observations of hands but rather is a formulaic imposition of a traditional Chinese system of correspondences onto the hand. In other words, some people, such as Terence Dukes, believe that the *ba gua* were distributed on the palm and dorsum of the hands based on pure theory without regard to clinical experience, and certainly this is one of the dangers and abuses of systems of correlative thinking. Whether this system was derived first from observations of real peoples' hands, which were later systematized or whether this system was arbitrarily imposed upon the hand due to the zeal of Song Dynasty Neoconfucianists is a question beyond the expertise of the authors.

Because this system's indications are different from and, in some cases, diametrically opposed to the indications of the five phase system that forms one of the main sections of this book, these two systems are irreconcilable. Thus one cannot use both these systems at the same time. Although there are many points of view about the finer shades of interpretation of the shapes of the hands, fingers, mounts, and lines used in five phase palmistry, still there is an almost universal agreement East and West about the basics of reading these appearances. Therefore, we feel that the system of five phase palmistry (related as it is to Western and Ayurvedic palmistry) is more reliable. However, because the eight trigram system is used therapeutically in Chinese pediatric massage (*xiao er tui na*) and because pictures of this system appear in various English language books on Chinese palmistry, we have included this system as an appendix for historical and research purposes.

In this system, the palm of the hand is divided into eight sections or areas and each one of these eight areas is associated with one of the *ba gua* or eight trigrams of the *Yi Jing (Classic of Change)*. These eight trigrams are a very ancient system of symbolism. It is believed that all phenomena in the universe correspond with one of these eight symbols. Any two things that are related to the same *gua* or trigram are believed to co-respond or resonate together. This is because they share a similar principle in their creation and function.

In terms of Chinese medical palmistry, this system of dividing the various areas of the palm according to the eight trigrams primarily bases its readings on the color and luster and the sinking or bulging on each location as well as any prominent blue veins appearing on the surface. A healthy, lustrous, rosy color, a normal bulge, and lack of prominent blue veins are all signs of good health and normalcy in the organs and functions associated with the trigram that rules that area. While abnormal colors, sunken flesh, and prominent blue veins suggest disease in the organs and functions associated
with the ruling trigram of that area.

The Eight Trigrams on the Palm

1. *Zhen,* the Arousing, Thunder

Location: The inner and upper part
of the thenar eminence

Five phase correspondence: Wood

Zhen location on the palm

Bodily correspondence: This trigram represents the function of the nervous system.

Indications: Generally, when this location is bulging with a red, ruddy color, the health is good and the nerves and spirit are normal.

If the lines are scattered with cross-shaped lines, star-shaped lines, and hair-shaped lines, this indicates nervousness from an imbalanced lifestyle. This type of individual will tend toward neurosis.

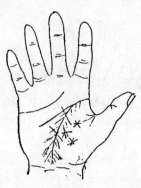

If this area is pale with no strength, the flesh hard or thin, and the area surrounded by the thenar eminence very narrow, this indicates a tendency toward reproductive and endocrine dysfunction.

Cross-shaped lines, star-shaped lines, & hair-shaped lines on the *Zhen* location

2. *Sun,* the Gentle, Wind

Location: On the palm under the index finger

Five phase correspondence: Wood

***Sun* location on the palm**

Bodily correspondence: This trigram represents the liver and gallbladder.

Indications: Generally, if this location is bulging with a ruddy, red color, the liver and gallbladder function are fairly good.

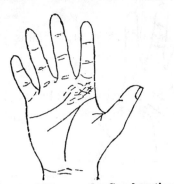

If the lines are scattered and the skin is rough with a dark color, this indicates that liver function is relatively weak.

Scattered lines on the *Sun* location

189

3. *Li,* the Clinging

Location: On the palm under the middle
and ring fingers

Five phase correspondence: Fire

Bodily correspondence: This trigram is representative
of the heart. It is also associated with the blood
circulation and eyesight.

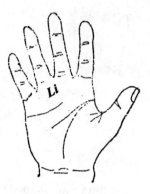

Li location on the palm

Indications: If this area is bulging, the color is a healthy, fresh color and there are no scattered
lines, it indicates good heart function. It further indicates good eyesight.

If the lines are scattered with a dark color, then the heart function is relatively weak.

Scattered lines on the *Li* location

If this area is recessed and sunken with blue
veins showing on the surface, it usually
indicates that the heart's strength is weak or
that heart fire is exuberant.

←

4. *Kun,* the Receptive

Location: On the palm under the small finger

Five phase correspondence: Earth

Kun location on the palm

190

Bodily correspondence: This trigram is representative of the abdominal organs in general and the spleen and stomach in particular.

Indications: If this area is bulging with a healthy, fresh color, it indicates that stomach and intestinal function and urological and reproductive systems are normal.

If the lines are scattered and there is a dark-colored, rough skin, this indicates that the functions of the large and small intestines and urological system are relatively weak.

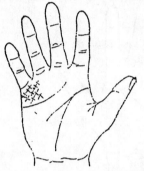

If the area is recessed and sunken with blue veins and bones near the surface and if the skin is dry with no blood color, it indicates that the reproductive function is relatively weak. Females with this sign will often suffer from infertility due to cold uterus, one of the causes of female infertility in TCM.

←

Scattered lines on the *Kun* location

5. *Dui*, the Joyous, Lake, Marsh

Location: Under the small finger, between the heaven crease and the human crease, near the side of the palm, below the *Kun* location

Five phase correspondence: Metal

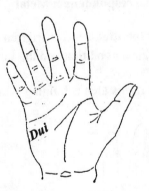

***Dui* location on the palm**

Bodily correspondence: This trigrams is representative of the lungs and large intestine.

Indications: If this area is bulging with a healthy, fresh color, it indicates good health.

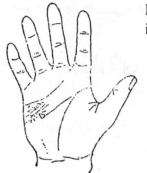

If the lines are scattered, the skin is rough and the color is dark, this indicates that the function of the respiratory system is relatively weak.

If the area is recessed and sunken, with blue veins and bones near the surface, and with dry, pale skin, it indicates that there is a respiratory system infection or pulmonary emphysema.
←

Scattered lines on the *Dui* location

6. *Qian*, the Creative

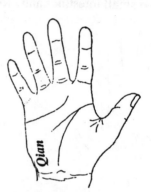

Location: Under the *Dui* location, above the wrist crease

Five phase correspondence: Metal

Qian location on the palm

Bodily correspondence: This trigram represents both the psychological condition and the lungs.

Indications: If this area is bulging with a healthy, fresh color, it indicates good health.

If there are scattered lines and the skin is rough with dark color, it usually indicates that the individual is overly emotional. It also shows the tendency for qi depression and neurasthenia.

If the area is recessed and sunken, with blue veins and bones near the surface, and with dry, pale skin, this indicates that a weak respiratory system has affected the health.
←

Scattered lines on the *Qian* location

7. *Kan,* the Abyssmal

Location: Below the middle of the palm

Five phase correspondence: Water

Bodily correspondence: This trigram is associated with the kidneys and bladder and the condition of urological and reproductive systems function.

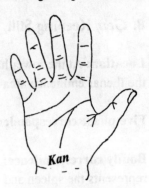

Kan location on the palm

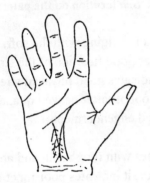

Indications: If the area is bulging with the flesh that is soft and smooth, it indicates good urological and reproductive system functioning.

Scattered lines and skin that is rough with a dark color indicates that nutrition during childhood was poor. It further shows a weak physical condition that in adulthood will show a tendency to fatigue easily due insufficient original qi.

Scattered lines on the *Kan* location

Blue veins visible on the surface of the skin with recessed, sunken, very thin flesh indicate a weak urological and reproductive system. ➡

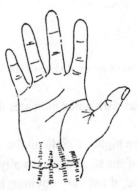

Blue veins on the surface of the *Kan* location

If the wrist creases are scattered and incomplete, it usually indicates insufficient function of the kidney. There is also a tendency toward infertility if the defect in this area is very serious.

8. *Gen,* Keeping Still, Mountain

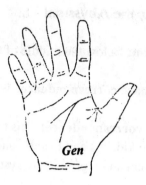

Location: At the lower half of
the thenar eminence area

Five phase correspondence: Earth

Bodily correspondence: This trigram
represents the spleen and stomach.

Gen location on the palm

Indications: If this area is bulging with the soft,
smooth flesh, it indicates good function of the stomach
and spleen. It further indicates good physical strength
since the spleen is the root of latter heaven qi and
blood transformation and engenderment.

If there are scattered lines with rough skin and an oval-
shaped area of dark color, it indicates poor function of
the spleen and stomach.

Scattered lines or oval-shaped dark color on the *Gen* location

An obvious dark color indicates that gastric disease is present.

If veins are highly visible on the surface and the area is recessed, sunken, and thin, then the
function of the stomach is usually insufficient. Generally, veins may be slightly visible on the
surface and, if not very obvious, have no significance.

In addition, the center of the palm is called the *Ming Tang* or Bright Hall and is associated with
the number nine.

9. *Ming Tang,* Bright Hall

Location: In the center of the palm

Five phase correspondence: Fire

Bodily correspondence: This area corresponds to
the condition of the heart and blood vessels as
well as to mental health.

Location of the *Ming Tang*

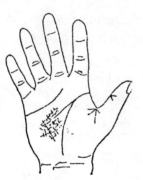

Indications: This area should normally be recessed
and somewhat sunken. If the *Ming Tang* is deeply
recessed and sunken with the flesh around it bulging
and the lines on it very clear, this indicates good
health, stable emotions, and a happy nature.

Scattered lines here indicate that the seven emotions
are disturbed and depressed. The individual may suffer
from insomnia and weakness.

Scattered lines or a dark green color at the *Ming Tang*

A dark green color on the *Ming Tang* indicates that illness is on the way. The *Ming Tang* is
where the heart fire is emitted. Therefore, if the center of the hand feels steaming hot, this
indicates vacuous fire rising. This usually appears in vacuity diseases such as sympathetic
nervous system dysfunction or chronic consumptive disease.

If the *Ming Tang* is icy cold and the palm is dry and pale, this is due to insufficient heart fire or
spleen/kidney yang vacuity. This may then manifest as weakness in the function of the
circulatory system or low digestive and endocrine function.

195

Index

I, J

K

L

palm, shapes of lines in the 54
palm, spoon-shaped 48
palm, square 48
palm, thickness of the 47, 52
palmar tinea 49
Palmistry & Health 7
palmistry, eight trigram 121, 187
palms, chronology & the lines on the 111
palms, edema of the 49
palms, widening & thickening of the 49
pancreatitis 126, 135, 167, 168
pancreatitis, chronic 167, 168
paralysis 59, 145
paranasal sinusitis 133
parasitic disease 33, 76, 80
pediatric massage, Chinese 187
pellagra 33
periodontitis 133
photophobic 82
physical condition, poor 25
physical strength, weak 38, 80
pleurisy 43, 134
pneumonia, acute 38, 76
pneumonia, lobar 35
poisoning, arsenic and lead 33
poisoning by various medicines or nicotine 33
poisoning, nitrite 36
pressing 34, 117, 129-131
prints, arch-shaped 26, 27
prints, whorl-shaped 26, 28
progesterone level, low 107
prostatic hypertrophy 173, 174
prostatitis, chronic 173
psoriasis 30
psychataxia 100
pulmonary abscess 21
pulmonary emphysema 35, 134, 192
pulmonary tuberculosis 17, 21, 33, 34, 43, 78, 124, 134, 151, 152
pulmonary heart disease 21
pushing 129-131
pyloric disease 135
pyocyanic infection 35

Q

qi & blood signs 123
qi and blood depression and blockage 34
qi, insufficient righteous 91
qi stagnation 6, 36, 41, 140, 159, 162, 165, 166, 172, 173
qi vacuity 32, 38, 52, 87, 157, 172, 173
Qian 121, 192

R

Raynaud's disease 35, 36
renal failure, chronic 37
reproductive and urological system diseases 61
reproductive function, weak 74, 109
reproductive system function, weak kidney and 24
respiratory diseases 15
respiratory tract, infectious diseases of the trachea and 61
rheumatic arthritis 135
rheumatic complaints 78
rheumatic fever 51
rhinitis 133, 142, 143
rhinitis, chronic 142, 143
rubbing 129, 131
Ryukyu Islands 4

S

salpingitis 175, 176
san cai 67
san gang 67
san hou 4
schizophrenia 30
Secret Tricks for Diagnosing Hundreds of Diseases by Yourself 7
Secrets of Success in the Four Examinations in Minute Detail 4
senile dementia 30
sex, dislike of 109
sex drive, lack of 109
Shang Han Lun 2
Shen Xiang Chuan Pian 3

OTHER BOOKS ON CHINESE MEDICINE
AVAILABLE FROM BLUE POPPY PRESS
1775 Linden Ave ○ Boulder, CO 80304
For ordering 1-800-487-9296
PH. 303\447-8372 FAX 303\447-0740

THE HEART & ESSENCE Of Dan-xi's Methods of Treatment by Zhu Dan-xi, trans. by Yang Shou-zhong. ISBN 0-936185-50-3, $21.95

HOW TO WRITE A TCM HERBAL FORMULA A Logical Methodology for the Formulation & Administration of Chinese Herbal Medicine in Decoction, by Bob Flaws, ISBN 0-936185-49-X, $10.95

FULFILLING THE ESSENCE: A Handbook of Traditional & Contemporary Chinese Treatments for Female Infertility by Bob Flaws. ISBN 0-936185-48-1, $19.95

STATEMENTS OF FACT IN TRADITIONAL CHINESE MEDICINE by Bob Flaws. ISBN 0-936185-52-X, $10.95

IMPERIAL SECRETS OF HEALTH & LONGEVITY by Bob Flaws, ISBN 0-936185-51-1, $9.95

THE MEDICAL I CHING: Oracle of the Healer Within by Miki Shima, OMD, ISBN 0-936185-38-4, $19.95

THE SYSTEMATIC CLASSIC OF ACUPUNCTURE & MOXIBUSTION by Huang-fu Mi, trans. by Yang Shou-zhong and Charles Chace, ISBN 0-936185-29-5, hardback edition, $79.95

CHINESE PEDIATRIC MASSAGE THERAPY A Parent's & Practitioner's Guide to the Treatment and Prevention of Childhood Disease, by Fan Ya-li. ISBN 0-936185-54-6, $12.95

RECENT TCM RESEARCH FROM CHINA trans. by Bob Flaws & Charles Chace. ISBN 0-936185-56-2, $18.95PMS: Its Cause, Diagnosis &

Treatment According to Traditional Chinese Medicine by Bob Flaws ISBN 0-936185-22-8 $18.95

EXTRA TREATISES BASED ON INVESTIGATION & INQUIRY: A Translation of Zhu Dan-xi's *Ge Zhi Yu Lun*, trans. by Yang Shou-zhong & Duan Wu-jin, ISBN 0-936185-53-8, $15.95

A NEW AMERICAN ACUPUNCTURE: Acupuncture Osteopathy, by Mark Seem, ISBN 0-936185-44-9, $19.95

SCATOLOGY & THE GATE OF LIFE: The Role of the Large Intestine in Immunity, An Integrated Chinese-Western Approach by Bob Flaws ISBN 0-936185-20-1 $14.95

MENOPAUSE, A Second Spring: Making A Smooth Transition with Traditional Chinese Medicine by Honora Wolfe ISBN 0-936185-18-X, 4th edition, $14.95

MIGRAINES & TRADITIONAL CHINESE MEDICINE: A Layperson's Guide by Bob Flaws ISBN 0-936185-15-5 $11.95

STICKING TO THE POINT: A Rational Methodology for the Step by Step Administration of an Acupuncture Treatment by Bob Flaws ISBN 0-936185-17-1 $14.95

ENDOMETRIOSIS & INFERTILITY AND TRADITIONAL CHINESE MEDICINE: A Laywoman's Guide by Bob Flaws ISBN 0-936185-14-7 $9.95

THE BREAST CONNECTION: A Laywoman's Guide to the Treatment of Breast Disease by Chinese Medicine by Honora Lee Wolfe ISBN 0-936185-13-9 $8.95

NINE OUNCES: A Nine Part Program For The Prevention of AIDS in HIV Positive Persons by Bob Flaws ISBN 0-936185-12-0 $9.95

THE TREATMENT OF CANCER BY INTEGRATED CHINESE-WESTERN MEDICINE by Zhang Dai-zhao, trans. by Zhang Ting-liang ISBN 0-936185-11-2 $18.95

A HANDBOOK OF TRADITIONAL CHINESE DERMATOLOGY by Liang Jian-hui, trans. by Zhang Ting-liang & Bob Flaws, ISBN 0-936185-07-4 $15.95

A HANDBOOK OF TRADITIONAL CHINESE GYNECOLOGY by Zhejiang College of TCM, trans. by Zhang Ting-liang, ISBN 0-936185-06-6 (2nd edit.) $21.95

PRINCE WEN HUI'S COOK: Chinese Dietary Therapy by Bob Flaws & Honora Lee Wolfe, ISBN 0-912111-05-4, $12.95 (Published by Paradigm Press, Brookline, MA)

THE DAO OF INCREASING LONGEVITY AND CONSERVING ONE'S LIFE by Anna Lin & Bob Flaws, ISBN 0-936185-24-4 $16.95

FIRE IN THE VALLEY: The TCM Diagnosis and Treatment of Vaginal Diseases by Bob Flaws ISBN 0-936185-25-2 $16.95

HIGHLIGHTS OF ANCIENT ACUPUNCTURE PRESCRIPTIONS trans. by Honora Lee Wolfe & Rose Crescenz ISBN 0-936185-23-6 $14.95

ARISAL OF THE CLEAR: A Simple Guide to Healthy Eating According to Traditional Chinese Medicine by Bob Flaws, ISBN #-936185-27-9 $8.95

PEDIATRIC BRONCHITIS: ITS CAUSE, DIAGNOSIS & TREATMENT ACCORDING TO TRADITIONAL CHINESE MEDICINE trans. by Gao Yu-li and Bob Flaws, ISBN 0-936185-26-0 $15.95

AIDS & ITS TREATMENT ACCORDING TO TRADITIONAL CHINESE MEDICINE by Huang Bing-shan, trans. by Fu-Di & Bob Flaws, ISBN 0-936185-28-7 $24.95

ACUTE ABDOMINAL SYNDROMES: Their Diagnosis & Treatment by Combined Chinese-Western Medicine by Alon Marcus, ISBN 0-936185-31-7 $16.95

MY SISTER, THE MOON: The Diagnosis & Treatment of Menstrual Diseases by Traditional Chinese Medicine by Bob Flaws, ISBN 0-936185-34-1, $24.95

FU QING-ZHU'S GYNECOLOGY trans. by Yang Shou-zhong and Liu Da-wei, ISBN 0-936185-35-X, $21.95

FLESHING OUT THE BONES: The Importance of Case Histories in Chinese Medicine by Charles Chace. ISBN 0-936185-30-9, $18.95

CLASSICAL MOXIBUSTION SKILLS IN CONTEMPORARY CLINICAL PRACTICE by Sung Baek, ISBN 0-936185-16-3 $10.95

MASTER TONG'S ACUPUNCTURE: An Ancient Lineage for Modern Practice, trans. and commentary by Miriam Lee, OMD, ISBN 0-936185-37-6, $19.95

A HANDBOOK OF TCM UROLOGY & MALE SEXUAL DYSFUNCTION by Anna Lin, OMD, ISBN 0-936185-36-8, $16.95

Li Dong-yuan's **TREATISE ON THE SPLEEN & STOMACH**, A Translation of the *Pi Wei Lun* by Yang Shou-zhong & Li Jian-yong, ISBN 0-936185-41-4, $21.95

PATH OF PREGNANCY, VOL. I, Gestational Disorders by Bob Flaws, ISBN 0-936185-39-2, $16.95

PATH OF PREGNANCY, VOL. II, Postpartum Diseases by Bob Flaws, ISBN 0-936185-42-2, $18.95

How to Have a HEALTHY PREGNANCY, HEALTHY BIRTH with Traditional Chinese Medicine by Honora Lee Wolfe, ISBN 0-936185-40-6, $9.95

MASTER HUA'S CLASSIC OF THE CENTRAL VISCERA by Hua Tuo, translated by Yang Shou-zhong, ISBN 0-936185-43-0, $21.95

PAO ZHI: An Introduction to the Use of Processed Chinese Medicinals to Enhance Therapeutic Effects by Philippe Sionneau, translated by Bob Flaws, ISBN 0-936185-62-7, $34.95

THE BOOK OF JOOK: Chinese Medicinal Porridges, A Healthy Alternative to the Typical Western Breakfast by Bob Flaws, ISBN 0-936185-60-0, $16.95

SECRET SHAOLIN FORMULAS FOR THE TREATMENT OF EXTERNAL INJURY by De Qian, translated by Zhang Ting-liang and Bob Flaws, ISBN 0-936185-08-2, $18.95

CHINESE MEDICINAL WINES & ELIXIRS by Bob Flaws, ISBN 0-936185-58-9, $18.95

THE DIVINELY RESPONDING CLASSIC: A Translation of the *Shen Ying Jing* from the *Zhen Jiu Da Cheng* by Yang Shou-zhong & Liu Feng-ting, ISBN 0-936185-55-4, $18.95

THE SYSTEMATIC CLASSIC OF ACUPUNCTURE & MOXIBUSTION by Huang-fu Mi, trans. by Yang Shou-zhong & Charles Chace, ISBN 0-936185-29-5, $79.95

AGING & BLOOD STASIS: A New TCM Approach to Geriatrics by Yan De-Xin, ISBN 0-936185-63-5, $21.95